Austerity Dairy from Lavender Cottage

Hastings 1947

By Victoria Seymour

To the Boat House.
Hastings

Victoria Seymour

First published in 2009 By Victoria Seymour.

Copyright Victoria Seymour.

Email: mail@victoriaseymour.com

Website: www.victoriaseymour.com

ISBN 978-0-9543901-7- 4

A catalogue record of this book is available from the British Library.

Printed in Great Britain by

impression IT.
Unit 2
Maunsell Road,
St Leonards-on-Sea,
East Sussex.
TN38 9NL
Tel 01424-852116
www.impressionit.co.uk

This book is dedicated to the memory of the late Eleanor Ellis Russell of London, Ontario, Canada. Emilie Crane and Eleanor were cousins; they never met but shared the same great-great grandmother. Eleanor followed Emilie's Lavender Cottage life through the now famous letters, sent to her sister, Marion Ellis. Eleanor loved writing and wrote many poems, most of which are set to music that she composed. She had a great interest in Victoria Seymour's books and was pleased that through them the Crane family history was expanded upon.

My sincere thanks for help in creating this book go to Miss Joyce Brewer, Mrs Joyce White, Miss Beryl Cherry and Mr Richard Pitcairn Knowles for their memories of the Ridge, to Mr Ronald Burkin for his gardening tips and personal anecdotes, Brian Gasson for fishing advice and Trish Allchin for guidance on dementia. Thanks go also to the administrator of www.ukhomefront.co.uk for their permission to source the website's household hints

Special gratitude goes to Mrs Wendy Johnson, Emilie Crane's cousin, for approving the use of her family archives and for checking the manuscript.

I am grateful to Hastings Reference Library and to the Hastings and St Leonards Observer for the use of their archive. Also to Mr Dan Suri, Weatherman, for his report on the UK weather of 1947. My thanks to Colin Allchin, for his website services and to Angelique and Peter for their moral and practical support.

Emile Crane with James on the doorstep of Lavender Cottage

The Lavender Cottage Austerity Dairy

Lavender Cottage diary writer, Miss Emilie Crane, lived in Hastings with two other elderly women: Clare Marriott, a retired clerical worker like herself, and Miss Edith Lake, a person of private means.

All the local and national news items in the diary are historically accurate and named individuals in the diary are real people, most of whom were known to Emilie Crane.

New Year's Eve 1899

"Miss Crane, will you do me the honour of accepting my proposal of marriage?"

This astounding offer came from my superior, Mr Wren. Everyone in the office, except he and I, had left early, to make preparations for the evening; not only was it the turn of the year but also the century. I then realised that my fellow-employees' privileged departure had been a ploy on his part, to leave us in a situation in which he could propose to me. In the office, of all places!

He went on to refer to my intelligence, efficiency and good humour; I understood immediately that this was in reality the offer of the post as housekeeper and nanny to his four motherless little children; his wife had died in childbirth some months previously.

At first I was too stunned to speak and he took this silence as an indication of my being overwhelmed, as indeed I was; but not with the gratitude and joy that he seemed to presume would be a felt by a 28 year-old spinster on at last being offered matrimony. I was, in truth, nearly overtaken by the urge to laugh hysterically, a phenomenon which often accompanies shock, but I grasped sufficient control of myself to say I was very flattered, (sounding like the heroine of a cheap novelette, I thought), but I would have to decline, as the domestic life was not one for which I yearned. He thanked me for my frankness and departed the office with what dignity he could salvage from the situation. I went to the mirror to put on my hat and noticed that a smear of the red ink, which I had spilled on my desk that afternoon, had made its way to the end of my nose. What I fool I looked; and he still proposed!

I could hardly wait to get back to our rooms to tell Clare about the whole fiasco. At first she was outraged at his audacity, whether for my sake or her own I could not tell. 'No mention in the proposal of love, I note', she said. Then she began to laugh about the ink, eventually saying, 'And what a comedown it would have been for you; from a crane to a wren!'

I dreaded going into the office again but Mr Wren behaved as if nothing unusual had taken place between us. A few weeks later I heard he was to marry a widow of well over forty with considerable means. I sometimes wonder how things would have turned out if I had accepted his offer. I do not think I would have been happy; I am rather awkward with babies and never wanted any of my own. But I do think of Mr Wren every New Year's Eve and hope that he found happiness.

January 1947

Clare and I stayed up last night to see the year in; Edith said that she would sit with us. At ten o'clock she went upstairs to get a shawl. When she did not come down, Clare peeped in to the bedroom and found her fast asleep on top of the covers. So she made Edith comfortable with a rug and a hot water bottle and left her to sleep the year away. We had been given some logs by kind neighbours, so we sat in the companionable firelight, with James sleeping in his favourite chair; how that cat loves comfort. We fell to talking about years gone by and friends from our office days. (I did not mention Mr Wren). It's said that people become nostalgic at Christmas time but in my case it's the New Year that stirs old memories. I am just so thankful to have Clare, my dear friend for over 50 years, with whom to share these reminiscences.

The first full year of peace is behind us, not that it has been an entirely happy time, much dreadful news from all over the world, while at home we have had continued hardships and shortages, which we are warned will get worse before they get better. As we were mulling over the past, Clare said how quickly time passes, that soon our lives would be over and there would be no record we ever existed. I said, 'What about our years of employment and the committee work for our church and St Catherine's Convalescent Home?' But she said that she meant our own daily lives, 'We having no children who would pass on the trivia of our existence.' I reminded her how often I write to family members and friends but she said it is hardly likely that these letters would be preserved for posterity. So I decided to keep a diary of sorts, rather like the Mass Observation scheme that began in 1937, but just for myself; jottings for my own amusement.

*

Clare and I have resolved to arrange for Edith to see her solicitor as soon as the weather improves. From time to time she talks about settling the legal aspect of our tenancy of Lavender Cottage, in case she goes before us. Perhaps we should have stayed in the bungalow Edith bought for us at Westfield Lane in 1928, when we retired from our office situations. But after her mother died in 1931 Edith felt so lonely that she wanted to come and live with us. Unfortunately, the bungalow was too small so she suggested it should be sold and between us we bought Lavender Cottage. Edith later gave us back the money that we had put into the building of an extension here and now we pay her a modest rent. Clare and I feel settled and will continue to do so if Edith keeps well, but her head is very bad; at times she cannot remember anything. The doctor says her brain arteries are hardening. Unless something is arranged we could be in a precarious legal situation when Edith goes. But I expect something will turn up.

Not that finding a new home these days is a simple matter. The daughter-in-law of our charwoman, Mrs Smith, and her two little children have lived with their grandmother since their house in St Leonards was bombed in 1943. All hoped that when Mrs Smith's son came home from the army it would mean that the young family would move out. But due to the terrible shortage of housing it will not come about for some time. Mrs Smith's house is so small and at their ages she and her husband find it exhausting to cope with the un-alloyed exuberance and turmoil that is part of young life. Houses are being built and repaired but so very slowly and there is a waiting list with certain priorities. No matter what the inconveniences being endured, young couples living with parents are considered to be suitably housed, so they are very low on the list.

Cousin Marion sent us the most wonderful parcel from Canada before Christmas. I don't know which we appreciated most, the cake or the eggs, the fruit or the meat, but it is no good me picking on anything as all were very wonderful. We rhapsodised over the milk and agreed it must be saved for times when cream should have been used. There's no Nestles Condensed Milk to be had here these days.

We intend to make a second Christmas with the parcel; the one which has just passed was so gloomy. A friend of mine had just lost her sister and her only living relatives are in America. She is very lonely so we invited her for Christmas and Boxing Days. Of course, any gaiety was out of the question, so now we have invited another friend, with whom we can share some of the good things in the parcel. I think that we did better in wartime as regards to food. The recent cut in the fat ration is particularly trying; if Clare were not such a good manager we should not enjoy any pastry at all. We should not grumble as people round here have been very kind and bring us some margarine if they can spare it.

I have just remembered; I won a pot of jam at a Boxing Day whist drive which I will bestow on a neighbour who is almost blind. She cannot make her own jam and as we have a fair amount of fruit from our summer garden I will be able to make sufficient for our own use. Our blackcurrant and gooseberry bushes are gratifyingly prolific almost every year and the rhubarb generally finds its way into jam, if we can get any ginger. Perhaps Cousin Marion will kindly oblige.

*

There have been sharp frosts and a thin layer of slippery snow on the Ridge footpaths, which keeps us indoors; Hastings Corporation does nothing for the roads up here and we older ones all fear falling in the street. I experienced enough of being in bed, suffering from shock, just before Christmas. I had been to visit an old lady in a nursing home and whilst walking home I took a short cut through the woods and fell into a muddy hole that reached above my knees. I got soaking wet and nearly ruined my dress and coat. How fortunate we are to have a dressmaker so close by. She soon restored my garments to some semblance of respectability and I made a good recovery from the shock. It's difficult to accept that one can no longer take the convenient little shortcuts through the woods and fields around here for fear of accidents. I think the deteriorating state of my feet was the real cause of my fall. They are stiff and painful and will not do as they are told. Added to this are painful chilblains. No wonder I wear carpet slippers all day. Clare, more self-disciplined than I, keeps to leather shoes. She says my chilblains are partly my own fault, as when my toes and fingers are cold I thrust them too close to the fire, allowing my extremities to warm up far more quickly than is good for the circulation.

*

Mrs Smith arrived late today, not surprising with the snow being so deep. Clare and I must cease referring to her as "The Blitz" and "The Bombshell" or we are going to let the names slip one of these days. But in truth Mrs Smith must be the most destructive force ever to wield a carpet sweeper, as our furniture bears witness; James is terrified of her; on her arrival at the cottage he hides. She comes twice a week, on Wednesdays and Thursdays, often turning up before her agreed hour saying, 'I like to make me mark early Miss Crane.' If I should catch Clare's eye on hearing this apt statement we can scarcely hold back the laughter.

5

Though not a churchgoer, Mrs Smith is given to singing hymns as she goes about her work, her favourite being "Onward Christian Soldiers." We suspect its martial tune and the bellicose turns of phrase spur her on to assault the furniture more vigorously. We are lucky to have Mrs Smith at all. Since the war, domestic help is very hard to come by, especially with our being so far out of town. Mrs Smith is 75 yet walks the two miles to here from the village and two miles back. Her knees are bad and she is blind in one eye but she is altogether very stoical; she has been with us for 14 years. This long acquaintance and the falling off of standards in deference since the war seem to encourage Mrs Smith to be somewhat forthcoming in her opinions. It makes Clare cross but I remind her that these are modern times and we and Mrs Smith are all elderly and the imminence of the Great Leveller puts a different complexion on things.

*

Mrs Smith was complaining about the state of our dustbin; we have had it for years and the bottom has almost fallen out. She noticed on her way here last Thursday that Scollay's, an ironmonger's shop a few yards away from our cottage, had received a rare delivery of dustbins, so we bought one immediately, "while stocks last", as the shop's sign declared. The bin seemed very flimsy, if that is the word for metal. On its return from the first trip to the dustcart it bore a large dent and the lid no longer fitted properly. When Clare remonstrated with the dustman he said. 'Don't blame me missus, blame Adolf Hitler, we dropped the best of our metal on him in the war.'

*

It is six years since we had such a winter as the one we are having now; my hands feel so frostbitten I can hardly write as my fingers are wrapped in bandages. We are not able to go out, the snow is so deep and the Ridge has no snow plough. Clare has just recovered from gastric flu but Edith is fairly well, if we may judge from her appetite! Food rations are still being decreased but through a friend we did obtain two chickens and one of my National Savings Group brought us six eggs. It was good of her as she is very poor. I feel so sorry for people; some have had no coal or wood for six weeks. We sent a neighbour some of our coal but could not give much as it is rationed. There are black market buyers here and it keeps prices to a prohibitive scale, when proper organisation of supplies would feed and warm many more. We are hoarding some of the contents of the parcels from Canada just in case the food situation becomes worse.

I read today in a letter from Marion of her friend Beatrice's theatrical experiences in connection with John Gielgud and of when he visited Canada. He is one of our best actors. I recall seeing him in The Importance of Being Earnest in a London theatre. I wish we had a good one at Hastings but the only suitable building has been turned into a cinema, now called the De Luxe. The conversion was quite unnecessary as there are five other cinemas in town. I should love to see a good play but London is too far for such a luxury.

Marion mentioned Niagara Falls in her letter and it reminded me of my visit there, accompanied by a mentally deficient but harmless young man. We sat on the edge of the falls, unromantically gnawing a cold chicken and afterwards went to the US side in the "The Maid of the Mist." We admired the view, which, I am sure, has now changed, as they seem to have built factories round about. We are reliably informed that the same kind of thing is planned for the Ridge.

I was sorry to read that Canada has been obliged to ration its people; she has been very good to us in many ways, both during and after the war. I must say that our present meat ration is not generous. How Clare manages to make it last us four days is a marvel to me. Although Edith had her own kitchen built onto the cottage, with a much bigger cooker than ours, she takes her meals with us these days as it's more sensible to combine our rations and make more satisfying meals. It's the people who live alone who are badly hit by the meagre rations; we were able to send one of them a tin of corned beef this morning. In what must have been a reckless moment the butcher brought us one last week.

*

The news today is not cheerful; the electricity is cut off for the day and we have neither candles nor oil. Torches and batteries are very scarce; it makes moving about the cottage in the dark rather risky. Gales are expected along our coast tonight but there are other people worse off; the sea is frozen at Folkestone but what can one expect at anything from 15 to 40 degrees. A village not far from here is cut off by snow drifts and there are 250 people there with only two loaves of bread between them. The River Thames is freezing but not yet to the point where they could roast an ox on it, as happened many years ago. I cannot write more; the daylight is fading and there is only the firelight to see by until the electricity comes on again. Edith has stayed in bed all day, not because she is ill but to keep warm. At least were able to fill hot water bottles and cook up some soup on the gas stove. We do not use the oven to heat the kitchen, as some do, as we feel it is against the principle of saving fuel.

*

We have been without sunshine for what seems like weeks; I miss the marvellous winter sunsets this year. With the Ridge being so high, on clear evenings we get a panoramic view of the setting sun. For a brief time the cottage interior is transformed, first to gold then rose-red. We stop what we are doing just to gaze out of the window. If only one could paint! The old folk around here call a spot on the Ore Place Estate, close to St Helen's Church, the Sunset Field. It faces south west and deserves its title; commanding, as it does, an uninterrupted view of the town and the seaward horizon. One local oldie mentioned that as a child he had observed from the field the spectacle of lurid and unearthly sunsets that followed the explosion of the Javanese volcanic mountain Krakatoa in August 1883. I too saw these skies, from London, when I was twelve years old.

*

It has been intensely cold; I read in the Hastings and St Leonards Observer that last Wednesday morning was the coldest so far, with 21 degrees of frost recorded at Alexandra Park. It is very dangerous to go about on foot or by vehicle and there were a number of accidents mentioned in the local paper; one fatal. A St Leonard's man, aged 76, went to clear the pavement outside his house and collapsed in the snow; it was some time before he was discovered. He was carried indoors and died of heart failure 15 minutes later. We three are beyond any such dangerous exertions and are lucky to have a twice-weekly gardener, Mr Clout, to help with our path clearing. Between times, for a few pennies, the newspaper delivery boy is happy to get to work with shovel and broom.

*

The Ministry of Food has just published a newspaper announcement about the latest values of food points. I do not know how Clare keeps up with it all but she has a wonderful head for figures. She has a folder that holds all her wartime recipes, Ministry of Food announcements and our ration books. She brings forth the folder every week and sits with pencil and paper, conjuring with rations, food point's allocation and money.

*

We have a most amiable girl who delivers the milk around here. She has been coming to us since the early part of the war, when she seemed hardly more than a child, never letting us down. Even in this terrible winter she has somehow got the milk to us. She has a sledge on board the van and if the side roads are impassable she drags the crates on the sledge. I do admire her spirit. I invited her in for a cup of cocoa the other day but she would not come into the cottage as her boots were clogged with snow. (I am sure they were men's boots but I did not say anything as I did not want to embarrass her). She told me her name is Joyce, while drinking her cocoa, standing on the door mat. I asked her if she had always wanted to be a milk girl and she said no, that she just fell into it. Joyce had been a pupil at the High School when the war began but evacuation upset her education; she was too young for the forces and so it was a matter of working at what she could. She supposed that helping to distribute food had been worthwhile war work. She's such an attractive girl and known hereabouts for her cheery manner and kindness. Joyce said that she was late on her round yesterday as an attempt to be a Good Samaritan led to disaster. She called at a customer's house on the West Hill, just as the daughter was setting off for her work at Plummer Roddis, a Hastings town centre department store. Joyce offered the girl a lift and off they went, unaware of the severity of the road conditions on the hill. A big lorry that appeared to be making its way up the steep Wellington Road was actually stuck in a four-foot snow drift, which then also trapped the milk van. Luckily there was a shovel on board so Joyce was able to dig out the van and its passenger. It was fortunate that there was no serious outcome from this misadventure; the local gossip around here is full of such happenings every day.

February

Miss Feather, our near neighbour, told me that Sir Charles Hill, the Radio Doctor, had been discoursing on chilblains this week. He said that he admitted he did not know much about them but believed that underfeeding, poor clothing and circulation played a part. He said that tight shoes and warming the hands and feet too quickly in front of the fire, instead of rubbing them to life, encourages chilblains. So Clare was right, as she so often is. Sir Charles said there is no cure but good food, warm clothing, such as woollen socks and gloves, help to prevent chilblains, as does regular exercise, to improve the circulation. He also said that the application of Hazeline Snow could bring some relief from the itching, burning and pain of the chilblains. I use Zambuk but it soothes only for a while.

*

Miss Feather is becoming rather anxious: Her father, for whom she kept house until his death last year, was a minister of the Methodist Church and their home, "Claremont", is the property of the church and used for the accommodation of the local minister. I expect she will have to leave the house. Existence can be very precarious for unmarried women, unless they have money; this is where Edith has an advantage.

*

We have been officially ordered not to use electricity during certain hours or waste electricity on needless lighting. The government is employing inspectors to see that people comply with the order; those who transgress are referred to in the newspapers as "pirates". There was a case in the local newspaper recently of a prosecution under the new regulation; it's like the return of the wartime blackout laws. We have a distant neighbour who was an Air Raid Warden in the war; he is an officious little man and I think he feels a loss of importance now that the war is over. Although his job in the food office should satisfy his need to control things! Mrs Smith came in yesterday bristling with outrage. Apparently the former warden had stopped her outside our cottage, to tell her to warn us that he had observed our landing light on for hours the previous night that he had made a note of it and would inform the authorities if it occurred again. He then reminded Mrs Smith that the penalty for the offence is a £100 fine or three months in prison. He showed her a notebook, with details of other Ridge "pirates."

We have been having very bad nights with Edith just recently and we have to leave the landing light on; only a very low wattage lamp. She wakes in the small hours and tends to wander about the house; if there is no light on we are afraid she will fall down the stairs. Mrs Smith's initial outrage increased with the passage of the morning, our furniture taking the brunt. As she put on her coat and hat before leaving she said that she was going to tell her son about that 'interfering squirt' and see what he thought about it. She posed, rhetorically, was that why he fought a war, got wounded and then shut in a German prisoner of war camp, to put up with spies at home?

The men returning from war are not to be trifled with. They are angry at coming back to no proper homes or jobs and poor food and do not take kindly to petty authoritarianism, unofficial or official. I do feel a certain amount of compassion for the former warden. Before the war his wife was a meek little thing, who devoted herself to his every need. But during the war she felt the urge to "do her bit" so she joined the Women's Royal Voluntary Service, a decision that wrought the most astonishing change in her. She learned to drive and started to wear makeup and even to entertain the troops, singing at the concerts the WRVS held in the local army encampments. She struck up a friendship with a Canadian soldier and before long the warden found himself short of a wife. Unable to cope alone on the domestic scene he moved in with his widowed sister, who has a house on the Ridge, and there he has remained. According to Miss Feather the sister is something of a martinet and bosses her brother about most fiercely. No wonder he wants to pass it on!

*

This is such a hard winter. We read that soldiers have been called out to destroy deep snowdrifts with flame throwers and factories are closed due to lack of coal and raw materials. Everybody is saying that except for the fact of there being no fighting and air raids, conditions are worse than in wartime. Morale is very low in some quarters. With the fading of patriotic fervour which attended the war, along with the feeling of us all being in it together, it is hard to endure post-war privations. Things are not helped by hearing our leaders expound as if they think there is some virtue of itself in austerity.

*

Yet another cut has been added to our list of miseries. The town is to adopt "a modified public lighting system" until the end of the present fuel emergency. Street lighting will be allowed to remain at road junctions, the town centre and to illuminate flights of public steps, of which Hastings has many. But most other places will be back to the wartime blackout state, with only the light from houses and passing vehicles to show the way. Of course, unlike the war years, people can use torches, if they can get the batteries. Every form of auxiliary lighting and heating is pressed into service to help save fuel. Clare issued a hollow laugh when she read in the local paper that council meetings in the town hall that are held after dark are conducted by candle-light and the councillors wear their official robes under their overcoats. Clare said, 'Why should they not? We sit in gloom until the fuel emergency restriction hours have passed and then go to bed wearing cardigans and dressing gowns over our nightdresses, as well as hats.' (Clare and I, looking ridiculous, retire wearing knitted caps. Edith, who chooses to preserve her vanity even while sleeping, has only a hairnet for comfort).

*

The local newspaper informs that the Master Bakers Association have announced that the fuel shortage means that our bakers will not be making cakes for some while but bread supplies will continue normally. This announcement does not give us any personal concern as Clare is able to turn out acceptable cakes, from modest ingredients, at a moment's notice.

*

The boxes in which the gifts arrive from Canada are so sturdy they are too good to put out for salvage. I got Clout to store them in the loft today and while he was up there I asked him to bring down a trunk of clothes that had belonged to my father. I cannot believe it will be 20 years this summer since he passed away. In the evening Clare and I went through the trunk to see what might be of use. I was astonished to find that some of father's winter clothing was intact, but we had packed them away with a generous supply of moth balls; you could still smell them, faintly, after all those years. I had a vision of Clout's thin legs, earlier in the day, dangling from the loft hatch and thought how cold he must get in this terrible winter, as he cycles to his various places of work.

We decided to give Clout the clothes. How to do it without embarrassing him and ourselves? We thought we would ask Mrs Smith's advice as she might have a good notion of how the procedure could be arranged. I also found in the trunk a navy blue summer coat, rather worn at the collar and cuffs, which I used to wear to the office. Of course it is very out of style but few of our age are concerned these days with such niceties. Edith is quite content to dress in the mode of years gone by, wearing an array of floating scarves and long strings of beads, presenting quite a hazard when jugs of custard or gravy are passed at table. Edith's maid, who comes in to help her in domestic and personal ways, seems to spend much of her time removing traces of recent meals from Edith's attire. I cannot see much else she does; apart from a little light dusting and tidying-up the muddles that her employer creates. Sometimes I do not know why Edith keeps her on; she never seems to do a full day now, though she is paid for it. Occasionally, the maid waves Edith's hair as she is forbidden to use the curling tongs. Edith scorched her table cloth with them last year and we are fearful she will set the house on fire! A barely concealed animosity simmers between the maid and Mrs Smith, who regards her as 'A useless article who is not worth her wages.'

*

Clare came up with a good notion today of how to pass on father's clothes to Clout without him losing face. We know from Mrs Smith that Mrs Clout is a devoted churchgoer, who gives much of her time and what money she can spare, to the poor of her parish; though goodness knows, she is not well off herself. Clout has fashioned a little wooden cart that he fixes to the rear of his bicycle to carry around his tools. I will parcel up father's clothes and leave them in the shed. Mrs Smith can tell Clout that they are for the village church jumble sale and will he take them to Mrs Clout; we will have to trust Providence that she takes the hint. This way pride is preserved should Clout wish to use them himself.

Mrs Smith, with her usual directness said, 'If he's got any sense he'll sell them clothes; good second hand stuff is hard to come by nowadays and no coupons neither.' At first I said to Clare that I hope Clout does not wear my father's jackets to work in the garden. Then I gave myself a telling off; so much has changed since 1927 and a war such as the recent one gives us all occasion to reconsider petty attitudes. It is more important that a person should be warmly clad rather than my sentimentality indulged.

*

This week's meat ration had so much bone and fat in it Clare said that we would have to suffer make-do meals and soup menus for a few days. This is where our store of vegetables comes to the fore, if the frost has left them alone

Make-do Soup

1 pint of stock or water
1 tablespoon of household milk
1lb mixed vegetables
Parsley or any other herbs available
1-1 1/2 teaspoons salt
2 tablespoons wheat meal flour

Put the stock or water on to boil
Wash and grate or shred the vegetables
Add salt and vegetables to stock, cook until tender and season.
Blend flour and household milk with 1 breakfast cupful of water and pour into the soup
Stir and cook for 3-5 minutes
Serve with parsley or other chopped herbs sprinkled on the soup

*

I entered my 76th year today. One does not expect any kind of birthday jollity at such an age but it was touching to have remembrances from the young people in the family. Clare had got our dressmaker to run up two flower-print overalls as a gift to me. The ones I wear now are a disgrace. I think I bought them in spring 1941, just before clothes rationing began; with many mendings since they have given good service. Edith was having one of her vague periods and had forgotten the date. On learning it was my birthday she insisted on bestowing upon me a green scarf that she no longer wears. She is kind and means well.

Clare made a nice tea for us all. She had turned out an excellent eggless sponge cake that was worthy of a generous layer of my blackcurrant jam. We listened to a talk and concert on the BBC Third Programme in the evening, even though the reception was poor, trying to forget about the weather. How much longer can this snow linger? The old adage about it waiting for more is proved every few days. We read in The Times recently that to help the nation the Welsh coal miners have agreed to work on Sundays for the first time ever. This must represent a sacrifice to a people to whom Sunday Observance is important; I see it as Christian act in its truest sense.

Eggless Sponge Cake.

6 ounces of self-raising flour with 1 level teaspoon baking powder
Or the same weight of plain flour with 3 level teaspoons baking powder
2 1/2 ounces of margarine
2 ounces of sugar
1 level tablespoon of golden syrup
1/4 pint milk or milk and water
Jam for filling

Sift the flour and baking powder
Cream the margarine, sugar and golden syrup until soft and light
Add a little flour then a little liquid, Continue this process until a smooth mixture is achieved
Grease 2 seven inch sandwich cake tins and divide the mixture equally between the tins
Bake for about 20 minutes just above the centre of a moderately hot oven until the tops of the cakes are firm to the touch
Turn out onto a baking rack and when cool sandwich the cakes with jam

*

Edith is Secretary to St Catherine's House Home for Gentlewomen; I also sit on the committee. I feel sorry for Edith as the convalescent home committee follows procedure with a fearful strictness that alarms her. Their meetings are also interminable; there are members who see it as their duty to oppose every proposal and contest every point. Edith gets very flustered while taking the minutes so I also discreetly take notes in order to help her to complete her report.

At this year's AGM our president, Lady Idina Brassey, suggested we should extend an invitation to the home's patroness, Princess Alice, Countess of Athlone, to visit the establishment again. Lady Brassey said that she recalled two visits from the Princess many years ago and now that she had returned to England from abroad she might care to make another. (At least this is what I think she said; her voice rarely rises above a whisper, so tiresome at meetings). The committee asked Edith to send the invitation. This will be another task for me as I know Edith will probably quake at the thought of writing to a Princess. We were told by the treasurer, Mr P Joy, that the residents of the home had numbered 87 during last year but there had been staffing problems and the account was in deficit to the sum of £28-4s-2d. The home's income had increased by £116 but expenditure was up, due to the increased costs of salaries and maintenance. All agreed that wider publicity was required to let it be known what accommodation is available. We then had committee elections and Edith and I, with several others, were re-elected. I do hope that we both continue to have the health to keep up our obligation.

On our church committee, Clare is treasurer, I am secretary, and Edith also sits. Here, too, the AGM is in February, so this time of year seems to be dominated by AGMs and reports. Our church committee is run more simply; the treasurer's report is always very straightforward under Clare's stewardship. It is remarkable the amount of events we undertake at the church and although so many of our members are getting on in years, the attendances at meetings and services are very good; our church also attracts a good number of visiting worshippers, on holiday in the area.

Our committee meetings always end with a good tea. Everybody contributes something with the result that we have a splendid variety of dainties to share. I usually prepare sandwiches and leave the cake-making to Clare. This year she is using a recipe that she found in one of the Ministry of Food leaflets. It has to be eaten up almost at once as the ingredients make for a rather dry result that has no keeping qualities. However, leftovers from a committee tea are unheard of!

Sugarless Sponge Cake

1 ounce cornflour
4 ounces flour
1/2 teaspoon baking powder
Pinch of salt
2 ounces margarine
1 fresh egg or dried egg equivalent
1 small tin sweetened skimmed milk
1 teaspoon lemon juice
A little lemon rind

Sift the flour, baking powder and salt together
Rub in the margarine
Add the egg well beaten
Lastly add the milk, lemon juice and zest
Bake in a greased sponge cake tin or two sandwich tins for 20 to 25 minutes at regulation mark 5
When cool either cut the cake in two or spread the two cakes with jam and sandwich together

*

There will be so much to carry to the church committee meeting tomorrow that we will have to hire a car, as we do for Sunday worship. One bus service does actually stop outside Lavender Cottage but it is so infrequent that organising convenient departure and return is difficult, particularly on a Sunday. But the bus is useful for shopping on weekdays, if one plans properly. There are buses numbered 6 and 11, which come up from the town, to a terminus at the distant cemetery gates. This service is fairly frequent but for us it means a walk to and from the bus stop; not congenial if there is bad weather or heavy shopping involved. The number 2, the service that stops outside Lavender Cottage, is a circular, arriving here every 45 minutes. We are fortunate in that this long road is punctuated by two villages, with a good variety of shops; Ore village to the east offers more choice. Often one can postpone a visit to Hastings for weeks, which is desirable in the season, when the town is so crowded. Our hired car is provided by Mr Milton who lives in Rock Lane. Mrs Smith told me that his house is called Stan-den-der, which I first thought was a foreign word, possibly Hindustani. I asked Mr Milton about this and he laughed and said the name was composed of the first syllables of the names of his three sons, Stanley, Dennis and Derek. Well, he will have plenty of help in his work when they grow up, if anybody can still afford taxis by then.

March

I have just discovered Mrs Smith's Christian name after all these years. When Clout comes to the back door for his mug of tea he knocks and says 'erm.' I thought until today that he was trying to attract somebody's attention. After he had gone back to the garden Mrs Smith said, 'I do wish he wouldn't call me Erm just because we was at infants' school together. Me proper name is Ermintrude; it took me mum and dad a long time to think up a name for me that's a bit different and I'm not having it messed about with. Right is right!'

At the time she was wearing the sacking apron and the oversize galoshes that she dons to scrub the kitchen floor and back steps so her dignified stance was a little compromised. But before I could respond to this outburst Mrs Smith said, 'And he's too forthcoming if you ask me. Last week he said them homemade oatmeal biscuits Miss Marriott gave him with his mug of tea was fit only to feed his rabbits.' I must tell Clare this as Clout's verdict on the biscuits matched ours. Unfortunately, Clare's ingenuity to find ways to reuse unsuccessful recipes and leftovers failed her this time and the oatmeal biscuits went out for the birds. I confessed that the fault was mine as when I copied out the recipe I forgot to include in the ingredients the required one tablespoonful of Golden Syrup.

Oatmeal biscuits.

4 ounces of flour
4 ounces of oatmeal
1/2 a teaspoon of salt
1/2 a teaspoon of baking powder
1 tablespoon of Golden Syrup
2 ounces of margarine
1 teaspoon of sugar.

Mix all the ingredients into a stiff dough with milk or water or half of each
Roll mixture on a floured board to about a quarter of an inch thickness
Cut into squares and place on a greased baking tin
Bake in a moderate oven for 15 minutes

*

We were fortunate in getting our two Annual General Meetings over before another heavy snowfall and severe frosts. Generously, Edith paid for a car for both journeys and the meetings were in daylight hours, when the cold is less intense. I was set to give a talk to our church Women's Literary Society this afternoon but I had to ring to say I would not be able to attend, as the condition of the Ridge is keeping me indoors. It is treacherous underfoot; a few days ago the rain froze as it fell, coating the snow with a thick glaze; the trees were also burdened with a weighty layer of ice. All day we could hear the dreadful sound of great branches breaking off with the weight of it and crashing to the ground. The brave, or should I say the foolhardy, ventured up to the Ridge to see the frozen landscape. Did they give a thought, I wonder, to the thousands of birds that died? I presume that those who came to see the sights walked, as the trolley wires were ice-encased. It was also impossible for private cars to negotiate the dangerous hills up to the Ridge.

A friend's niece, who is newly married and lives at Pett Level, says that due to the steep hills around there, the inhabitants have had no deliveries of food or anything else for several days; their little general store has run out of supplies. They have had no bread delivery and the niece has been making rolls, not very successfully, from some old flour and dried milk. The niece was very upset when she phoned her aunt; she had wondered why the birds were so still in the trees and discovered that they were dead, frozen upright on the branches. Mrs Smith told me that Ore Place, the mansion on the Ridge commandeered by the army in the war and still occupied by their clerical workers, was closed for several days due to the weather and the absence of public transport. When the workers returned the ice-coated branches and giant icicles were intermittently falling from the trees onto the drive at Ore Place. The staff was duly ordered to walk along the drive in single file so that if anything fell it would not injure a group. Clare and I laughed at that as it seemed typical army thinking!

*

I felt wretched at cancelling my talk but it turned out that only a few members were able to get to the church, for the same reason as myself. Studying the Hastings and St Leonards Observer one can discern that the town is a splendid place for talks. It seems that almost every club or society offers speakers, year round, on all manner of subjects; history, both local and general, music and all of the arts, politics and current affairs. There are also talks by well-known public figures, for the most part held at the White Rock Pavilion. One could make a positive career out of attending talks and thereby further one's education. But unless they are in the afternoon we are prohibited from attending because of the poor public transport. Occasionally, if Edith also wanted to hear an evening talk, she would hire a car for all of us, but this has not happened for some time.

*

I have been looking hopefully for the appearance of the big patch of snowdrops, which Clare planted as a birthday surprise for me by our front gate some years ago. For us and passers by, who stop to admire them, they are a delicate harbinger of spring. I wonder if the bulbs are frozen to death and we will not see them again. I have never seen the garden look so dead in March. Clout's chief tasks when he comes to us are anything else but gardening. We do not want to tell him not to come in this bad weather as we know he depends on the money and he is so good in helping with inside jobs. This week he distempered the pantry and did it much more tidily than I would have done. Mrs Smith makes a face when I announce I intend to do distempering as my enthusiasm overreaches my skill and the floor benefits from my efforts as much as the walls.

*

Clare's teaching Edith to knit as a change from her endless tapestry work has not been an unmixed blessing. I know that when I learned to knit in 1934 I was dreadfully tiresome with my tangles and muddles. Clare thought it would encourage Edith to make something that grew more rapidly than the cross-stitch, thatched cottage cushion cover, which has taken Edith more than two years to bring to a not even half-finished stage. Provided with some white wool, Edith began on a simple pattern for a baby coat, with the church bring and buy sale in mind. However, the dropping of stitches and misunderstood pattern instructions has turned Clare into an absolute slave to Edith's knitting needles. Her cries for help punctuate every concert or talk we try to listen to on the wireless in the evenings. Clare now resorts to hiding Edith's knitting bag when something of interest is coming up. Poor Edith, she is so absent-minded these days; she soon gives up her search and returns to the thatched cottage embroidery, leaving us in peace but also feeling slightly guilty for being so devious.

Clare has so many craftwork skills. She has tried her hand at metalwork and wood carving, with considerable success, and on the domestic front she will undertake almost any job. (Apart from distempering). She is, unlike me, completely self-sufficient. The only thing she does not do is the correspondence. When I take her to task about this she says, 'Well, you were the one who had the scholastic letter published in the Times so you are the professional.' My reminding her that the letter was published in 1920 and I did not get paid for it is regarded as being of no consequence.

*

At last the thaw has come, along with heavy rain. Hastings Town Centre has been flooded as the drains could not cope with the torrents of water. But this is as nothing compared with other places in the country. We heard a speech on the wireless by the Minister of Agriculture; a most gloomy account of flood damage, millions of cattle lost, the impossibility of saving crops and a consequent shortage of things one considers necessary to existence. So we went to bed somewhat downcast. In the morning our postman, still working at aged over 70, handed us a large parcel, remarking, 'It's heavy'. I presumed it was the wireless ordered by Edith Lake for St Catherine's, but it was not. 'It's from Canada!' said Clare. We were so excited! We thought we would never find an end to the things contained therein.

First we hauled out a wonderful, heavy roll of ham; then jellied chicken; what a sight for sore eyes after months of considering how to share 5 wafer-thin rashers of bacon per fortnight between three people. Clare pulled out one thing after another with her eyes gleaming. Our beef and mutton, which I suspect is horse, is mostly bones, our potatoes are damaged by frost and now only one ounce of cheese, all make for a poor table. We must not grumble. Hundreds have been made homeless by floods but at 500 feet above sea level all we have is a waterlogged garden. The rains have caused havoc everywhere; I do wonder how the farmers have the heart to carry on but the British are very resilient. I am in bed with a wretched cold and my friends dodge in every minute to ask, 'Are you covered up?' As, indeed, I am and not alone either. I do not share Edith's dislike of James in bedrooms so he spends almost all of his time curled up in the warmest spot on my eiderdown, making me slightly uncomfortable but I cannot, out of fellow feeling, dislodge the dear old cat. I think he regards my illness a treat!

*

We are very fortunate in being able to hear the BBC Third Programme more clearly than previously. I understand from the Hastings and St Leonards Observer that few are able to receive it around here and the paper's correspondence is full of complaint on the subject. Mrs Smith's son has a friend whose service in the army was with wireless. Said friend was sent to see us and he explained that we needed a different and larger aerial, which he would fit for 'a drink.' We consulted Mrs Smith on this curious form of payment and she explained that it did not mean a cup of tea but a sum of money sufficient to buy a pint or two of beer. I presume this is similar to the request, 'cross my palm with silver.' I gave him ten shillings, which we later learned was too generous, but the pleasure we have from the clear reception is beyond price.

*

Just towards the end of the school term I had an astonishing communication from Mr Curtis, the headmaster of Hurst Court School for Boys, very near here. One of the school's masters had been clearing his father's house after his death last December and discovered a collection of Boy's Own magazines of considerable vintage. The master had been reading these throughout the winter and had come across the play I had written that was published in the magazine in 1921. He was talking about the play and its author to a colleague who said he thought he had heard his aunt mention my name. It turns out she attends our church and sits with me on its committee. What an extraordinary co-incidence! To be brief: Mr Curtis asked if I would give permission for the play to be performed by the boys as their end-of-summer term entertainment. He said that he already had permission from the publishers of the magazine and as it was a private performance, with no tickets to be sold, they had no further interest. As a courtesy, he wished for my approval and would I like to take an interest in the production? Clare thought it would be a pleasant diversion. The play, called "Boy Wanted", about the quest for an office boy in a Victorian business, is described as a "breaking-up piece", the purpose it will serve at Hurst Court. It's a farcical comedy and should appeal to boys' minds. I do not know if my play has ever been performed before, the magazine had no way of contacting me as I have moved home several times since it was published.

*

Mr Curtis sent a car to take me to Hurst Court; Lavender Cottage is only a short distance from the school but I appreciated the kindness. I met the English master, Mr Smith, who will instruct the boys in producing my play; we were served tea in the headmaster's study. I found Mr Smith a most genial man, full of questions about the play, which I enjoyed answering. I had to smile when he asked if I had drawn any part of the plot from life. I told him that before my retirement I was the departmental manager in a scholastic agency. I had indeed been employed in an office during Victorian times but the establishment in my play is fictitious. (On reflection, there are elements of some people I had met in my working life in the play's characters). Mr Smith wondered if my agency had ever directed any pupils to Hurst Court. I said that it is very likely but having dealt with thousands of clients over so many years it is impossible to remember.

I was told that the auditions for the cast were in progress and there has never been such enthusiasm among the boys to appear in the end-of-year play. The eagerness to participate may be because several of the characters in the play are the same age as boys who will be performing, but there is even competition for the part of Aunt Maria. Mr Smith and I could have chatted for hours but he had his duties and I had promised to help Edith sort out some unwanted books and magazines for St Catherine's reading room. So away I went in style, motoring the 500 yards or so, back to Lavender Cottage.

*

With Easter approaching, I should order a supply of seed potatoes from Mr Scollay, who owns the ironmongers along here. My own were ruined in the frost. To keep up with the gardening tradition I like to plant my potatoes on Good Friday but everything is so behind this year and I wonder if the soil is warm enough. Mr Scollay is a most helpful man and is always willing to transport our heavier requirements to us in a wheelbarrow. One could talk to him for hours about gardening; he is quite the local expert.

One bright spot: The snowdrops at the gate are not dead. They recently put in a very late appearance. There were fewer flowers and the foliage looked very threadbare, if that is a word for leaves, but now we know they were not frozen to death and they will no doubt multiply over the years.

April

Easter did not bring us good weather. There was a cold wind, worsened by the altitude here, and frequent showers, so I did not get the potatoes planted on Good Friday. I went down to the shed this afternoon to ask Clout to do it tomorrow. He had been sawing up the branches that he and a neighbour had dragged here from the perimeter of the fields and woods, after the weight of the ice had brought them down. An excellent stack of logs has resulted, which will be useful next winter. Clout was cleaning his saw and making such a business of it that I remarked on how painstaking he was being; he said that was how he had learned to treat tools when he was the gardener's boy at the Hall. I did not ask which Hall, it's difficult at times to understand him as he has so few teeth. Perhaps he will be one of those to benefit from the new National Health Scheme when it starts next year. He went on to say he was taught that after garden tools have been used they should be washed, dried and rubbed with an oily rag, even the handles. I inspected the shed after he had cycled off and noted that our sparse collection of tools, some dating back many years, had all recently benefited from Clout's ministrations with the oily rag.

*

Clare and I went over yesterday to Landsdowne Terrace see our dressmaker, Mrs Jones, who had been trying to do something with my old navy blue coat. Apart from attending to the needs of her usual clients, this good lady makes the habits for the nuns at St Mary's Convent at Baldslow, not far from Lavender Cottage. I would have thought that the sisters could have made their own garments, but not all have a bent for needlework, as they had at the convent where I was a boarder. Not that I am any kind of needlewoman as a result of being a pupil there. My coat was ready; Mrs Jones had made a new collar and cuffs from some dark blue velvet and a set of covered buttons to match; it looked very smart and far too elegant for my hum-drum life. The cost for the work was very reasonable and when I asked Mrs Jones how much I owed her for the velvet she said that there was no charge! It seems she had been shortening some dark blue velvet curtains for a client and my coat benefited from the unwanted off-cuts. When I said that I hoped I would not meet the curtain owner when wearing the coat; Mrs Jones said it was unlikely, as she had moved to Eastbourne. The dressmaker was about to re-fashion a wedding dress from an ivory-coloured, pure silk Victorian nightdress. I thought it was a sin to cut it up; so much beautiful lace and embroidery but she intended to incorporate these in the new design. It seems that nightdresses lend themselves well to adaptation and many a bride and baptismal infant have made their appearance in church in what was formerly a lady's night attire. Mrs Jones said that she had read in a magazine that brides can hire a wedding dress from the Gainsborough Film Studios wardrobe department for as little as thirty shillings; for an extra payment the bride can add shoes, veil and headdress; no coupons required for anything. I cannot see Hastings brides using this service as the cost and inconvenience of travel would outweigh anything gained. On our way home we called on Mrs Todd, who is our friend and a near neighbour of Mrs Jones. She was not at home but we could hear her parrot, Laura, screeching within.

We passed by the house called "Northmead" and Clare started chatting about before the war, when it was a poultry farm, run by two ladies, the Misses Holdstock and Hobbins. They also took in summer visitors, accommodating them in former Great War army huts, where they slept on iron beds, probably of the same vintage as the huts. I suddenly recalled hearing these visitors in Mr Watson's shop complain about the hard beds and the fact that almost all of the meals at the farm seemed to consist of eggs; I do not think, with the present absence of eggs from the menu, that they would complain now! The chicken farm and holiday guests have long gone as have the two ladies; the house is now just a family home. The chicken farm-cum-summer-visitors enterprise ended before Mrs Todd came to the Ridge, with her back garden hens.

*

Pondering on the subject of the Ridge in the summer time I recall that in days gone by it used to be quite lively round here before the war. The schools put on sports days and fetes and in the holidays Sandrock Hall Preparatory School for boys had a number of events in the grounds. The establishment was owned by Mr Kingdon and Mrs Scott, whose nephew, the actor Richard Murdoch, used to come down in the season accompanied by Arthur Askey. He, Mrs Smith reliably informed me, appeared on the wireless with Richard Murdoch in a programme called "Bandwagon". One year, I think 1938, these two performers, joined by the Hastings Fol-de-Rols, put on a concert party in the gardens of Sandrock Hall. Absolute mobs turned up for the show and Mr Watson's little shop did a great trade in sweets and chocolates.

*

We went back to visit Mrs Todd this afternoon and to take her a mutton bone for Laura. The bird is 30 years old; I presume that is quite young for a parrot. We understand from Mrs Todd that Laura spends hours picking out the morsels of gristle from a meat bone. The parrot is not in the best of health and Mrs Todd, who dotes on her, worries constantly. Laura is rather profane and must surely have had a previous owner with lower moral standards than Mrs Todd. She has nephews but surely it would take more than the occasional visit to instil anything into a parrot's memory. Such a strange pet for someone like Mrs Todd, who is very mournful and given to looking on the black side of any situation. In spite of this she is very kind and we have been grateful to her on countless occasions for her help with shopping and other tasks, when we have all been ill at the same time. On her mantel shelf there is a photograph of a soldier in the uniform of the Great War. I do not know if this is the late Mr Todd or some other relative; Mrs Todd does not respond readily to personal enquires. I notice that her glance strays often to the photograph. I overheard a neighbour commenting on how often Mrs Todd goes to the Ridge stores each day, 'She buys just one or two things and in half an hour she is back again, she must be very absent minded.' I did not say anything; not wishing to gossip, but the truth of the matter is more profound than mere absent-mindedness. Mrs Todd spends much of her day on voluntary acts of neighbourliness, doing shopping for a number of sick and housebound people. She also does other tasks for them I am told; a little washing up and tidying. Although not a cheerful person, with almost nothing to offer in the way of general conversation, Mrs Todd is a great listener; a quality for which the sick and lonely value her greatly.

*

When I went out to post some letters this morning I met Mrs Pitcairn Knowles. We had a grumble at the short food rations we are all enduring. She said it does not affect her family in the same way as they are all vegetarians. As indeed are all the guests, perhaps I should say patients, at the Riposo Nature Health Cure Hydro. She said throughout the last winter they were refurbishing the establishment so have not had to worry about keeping a crowd of people warm.

Mrs Pitcairn-Knowles is a very popular neighbour, well known for her great kindness and interest in people. She asked after the Lavender Cottage household inhabitants' health and how we are managing for food. I told her Edith Lake is a vegetarian and gets a bigger cheese ration instead of meat. I did not say that sometimes Edith is so hungry she puts aside her principles and eats some of the delicious meat in our parcels from Canada. I did say that we are all used to having meals that are meatless and that Clare is running out of new ideas. Mrs Pitcairn-Knowles said that many years before the war her mother-in-law published two books on vegetarian cookery and although they are now both out of print she may have some copies about the place and she would lend them to us.

This afternoon I heard something thump on the door mat and it was a package containing the two books. One is called Sixty Favourite Riposo Vegetarian Recipes and the other Health Giving Vegetables. Clare looked through the books for an hour, giving forth the occasional 'hmm.' I do not know if this was of approval or not but no doubt we will soon find out if she has been inspired. If she decides to experiment I hope my vegetable plot will meet her requirements.

*

In his announcements to the congregation last Sunday the Rev Hilton reminded us that October brings the 80th anniversary of the laying of the foundation stone of our church. He suggested that we should set about raising funds for a commemoration of the event. The subject was much discussed at the following committee meeting and we decided that a number of endeavours should be set in train.

This evening we three discussed the matter at home and Clare says that she is keen for us organise a garden party to raise money; Edith thought it would be delightful and was full of very ambitious plans. Even though food is still rationed I am sure we will be able to find something to serve for a tea. Perhaps we can spare a few things from the Canadian Store Cupboard, as Clare calls my cousin's bounty. We will charge admission to adults and extra for the set tea. I hope that friends and neighbours will be kind enough to donate little items to sell and we will have a "guess how many peas in the jar" contest. With luck and favourable weather we may be able to get a garden produce stall together. I think that a date in early July will be appropriate; perhaps there will be strawberries by then. Mrs Cole, from our church, is sure to help and we can usually count on Mrs Todd to lend a hand, as long as she is not obliged to get involved in anything too jolly, thereby being expected to smile.

May

When the bitter and prolonged winter finally loosed its grip the spring came at us in a glorious surge. The garden at the front of the cottage is Clare's domain, mine being the vegetable garden at the back. I do, however, have climbing roses and various perennials bordering the vegetables, to adorn the view. The front garden seems at its best just now; wallflowers, tulips and narcissi are jostling for space with forget-me-nots, violas and flowering rock plants. The laburnums and hawthorn are in full bloom, adding to the wonderful perfume, which drifts into the house. No wonder people stop and stare at the display. If Clare is pottering about in the garden they compliment her on the lovely show. A feature that adds to the beauty of this part of the Ridge is the multitude of old and mighty trees; one would not have expected them to have reached such height and grandeur at a 500 feet altitude, frequently swept by gales. This year the birds do not seem to be so prolific; no doubt due the great numbers lost to the cruel winter. Never-the-less, the dawn choruses have been riotous; one can forget the inconveniences of living up here at times such as these.

*

I was trying to remember how long it has been since we spoke to a little child. At our ages, with most friends unmarried and all closer to death than birth, the very young seem to disappear from life. There are nieces and nephews with children but they are some distance away and all are so busy. With petrol being in short supply it means that visits are rare. Of course, with five boarding schools situated on the Ridge, we often see the pupils passing by. How odd that I, who spent my working life in an agency, which matched children with the appropriate boarding school, should find myself retired into the thick of it. Not that I have been into the schools around here. I notice that in spite of shortages they try to keep up standards in the matter of uniform but the behaviour of the pupils in public at times leaves something to be desired. Some do not wear hats when they go out and Clare saw a girl from St Mary's Convent eating a bun in the street last week!

Edith seems to have a constant craving for sweet things. Someone at church gave us a recipe for carrot fudge, a most unlikely sounding concoction. Even though we followed the recipe carefully it tasted dreadfully insipid and was entirely unpalatable. However, Clare, with her eye on economy, did not waste it. She stewed the despised carrot fudge with an early picking of gooseberries from the garden, adding a few clusters of elder flowers from a nearby hedge, to take off the fruit's tartness; the flowers were removed and the carrots and gooseberries pressed through a sieve to make a puree and left to set. Accompanied by blancmange, the new recipe appeared at supper, Clare telling Edith it was called "Gooseberry and Orange Surprise." Edith does not particularly care for carrots so the surprise was ours, when she ate a good helping, asking Clare how on earth she managed to get sufficient sweet oranges to make such a delicious dessert!

Carrot Fudge
4 tablespoons of finely grated carrot
1 gelatine leaf
orange essence or squash

Put the carrots in a pan and cook them gently for ten minutes in just enough
water to keep them covered
Add a little orange essence or orange squash to flavour the carrots
Melt a leaf of gelatine and add it to the mixture
Cook the mixture again for a few minutes, stirring all the time
Spoon it into a flat dish and leave it to set in a cool place for several hours.
When the fudge feels firm cut it into cubes

*

We have had a good crop of gooseberries every year since I took Clout's advice on combating the sawfly. He told me to make a solution of elder leaves and soap in hot water and to flick it onto the clusters of leaves on the gooseberry bushes. This is where the pest hides, eventually denuding the plant of its leaves and affecting its yield. What a wonderful tree is the elder, giving mankind so many gifts; one of which, it is said, is to keep witches at bay. I recall I mentioned this to Clout, pointing out, being in skittish mood, the notable absence of witches in the locality. (I am sure he thinks I am deranged). He said nothing on the subject but did advise that I should wash my hands immediately after using the soap and elder solution, as the juice of elder is very strong and can burn the skin, 'especially a lady's hands.' Mine are so unsightly from the effects of arthritis and rough from gardening that I hid them under my pinafore as he spoke. Elder leaves are abundant but soap is in very short supply. We use every morsel; the last slivers are put in a jar and covered with water and in few days they form a soapy jelly; useful for washing up and, it seems, sawfly killing.

There is any amount of blossom on the elder trees this year. I love the perfume; I think it smells like wine but Edith says to her it's like tom cats! At any rate, there should be a wonderful crop of elder berries this autumn. I have put them in my chutney, when sultanas are in short supply. Clare uses them dried, in cakes, instead of currants. They do not have the flavour of currants; it's more the thought than the fact! We get cross, however, when the birds, having eaten the berries, leave an elderberry tinted "gift" on the bed sheets hanging out to dry.

*

A new wireless programme began last year. It is called Woman's Hour and Edith has become very fond of it. She asks if she can listen to it in our sitting room and if we are already ensconced for the afternoon we have to hear it too. It is transmitted between two and three o'clock and it seems to me to be mainly for the young married woman, as it broadcasts much about babies, husbands, clothes, cosmetics and housewifely skills for the uninitiated. Clare and I could hardly suppress our laughter when they announced a forthcoming piece on how to knit your own stair carpet. We are hoping Edith will not take up the idea! She likes the medical talks and became most engrossed in a talk on the menopause, a matter of mere historical interest to us three. I wonder if it is really quite the thing to broadcast a talk on such a subject into people's homes. Perhaps I am a prude; like the member of Miss Feather's church choir, who refused to sing O Come All Ye Faithful when they went out carol singing house-to-house, saying, 'The words virgin and womb are not a part of my outdoor vocabulary.'

*

We had what we believed to be a luxury dish for lunch today; cream of asparagus soup. After Edith and I had drunk the last drop Clare told us that the delicious fragments of "asparagus" were in fact the tips of the new shoots from a wild hop vine, which has seeded itself in the hedge at the bottom of the garden; brought here on a breeze, no doubt. When I first spotted it I did not know what it was and actually encouraged it, thinking that a vine which intertwined with the hawthorn hedge would make a useful windbreak. However, the dratted thing has taken over. So I was pleased to learn it has a culinary use but Clare said the new addition to her cookery repertoire would not appear frequently because she thought that only the first shoots of the season are fit to eat. At least the vine gives Miss Feather some sprays of hop flowers in September to decorate her church for Harvest Festival. The "cream" in the soup was a dash of evaporated milk from one of Marion's parcels; the remaining milk will make nice custard to go with stewed rhubarb; our garden is providing an abundant supply this year.

*

When I was writing letters this afternoon I heard Clare give a derisive hoot when she was going through The Times. She read out that the Bishop of London blames Hollywood films for Britain's high divorce rate. One does not have to be married to understand the toll taken on marriage by a protracted war, with long separations of couples and loneliness allied to temptation. And, of course, the divorce reforms add to the high figures. Are bishops trained in spouting nonsense, I wonder?

*

It was Edith's 77th birthday this week; her sister and brother-in-law arrived quite early in the day, on a surprise visit. Surprises are not a good thing for Edith in her condition and she was thrown into a state of panic at their unexpected appearance. The visitors presented her with a bouquet and a promise of a day out. This consisted of a drive in the country, lunch at the Fairlight Lodge Hotel and Country Club, followed by a matinee of the Hastleon's production of the musical comedy, "Les Cloches de Cornville" at the White Rock Pavilion. They had booked all this in advance, by telephone, from their London home. The sister said, 'We have reserved the best theatre seats costing almost five shillings each!'

Coming out of the blue, any one of these treats was more than Edith could cope with. I did warn her sister about Edith's state of mind, but as she looks physically well, my concerns were dismissed with the remark that everything was arranged, so away they all went. The maid took the opportunity to give Edith's sitting room a good turn out and in doing so found five one pound notes stuffed inside a vase. Clare and I had spent days looking for this "lost" money on Edith's behalf and had eventually concluded that she must have imagined having it in the first place. We decided to keep the rescued notes safely until Edith next needed to buy something important.

When the birthday celebrants returned at 5.30pm Edith was exhausted and miserable and her sister was furious. At lunch, already confused, Edith had made a noisy fuss about where to sit in the restaurant and what to eat. During the matinee Edith had fallen asleep and snored loudly during one of the tender moments of the story. She then awoke and created a drama of her own as she did not know where she was. The sister asked us why we had not told her how changed Edith had become. We did not remind her that we had attempted to do so. However, she was more concerned at ranting than addressing the subject of Edith's condition. It was not a happy day for her and she was glad to be ushered early to bed with a bowl of her beloved bread and milk. Next day all Edith could remember of the operetta was a 'beautiful young man who sang lovely songs.' According to the theatre programme this was the local baritone Steven Brewer; Mrs Smith says her niece knows of him and he is 'very handsome.'

*

It is now the Whitsun Bank Holiday; I am sure that last week was the hottest weather we have seen so far this year but Friday brought a cooling and welcome breeze. No doubt, regardless of the weather, the visitors and day trippers will still come. Clare's family telephoned to say they may motor down to see her if they have enough petrol.

*

There much discussion in the local press about a proposal to use the Grange School for Boys in Grange Road, and other places on the Ridge, for light industry. Mr Vernon Symonds, who owns nearby Netherwood Guest House and is now a town councillor, wrote to the local paper last week in support of the proposition. He believes it would provide much needed employment. One must not be selfish but a factory, if that is what it is to be, will certainly change the tone of the area. I have heard that as a result of the school being commandeered by the army during the war, and the grounds being used for a prisoner of war camp for Germans and Italians, much is ruined. It is said it will require thousands of pounds to restore it to its former use as a school. Such a pity; it was a fine building with lovely gardens.

June

Clare and I took the bus to Hastings this afternoon. It was a very hot day; the views from the Ridge over the town and sea are superb. In the narrow High Street, in the very old part of the town, it was the driver's misfortune to meet a bus going in the opposite direction. The road is scarcely wide enough to allow one bus through let alone a pair to pass each other. When this situation occurs there is much manoeuvering until a spot is found where the buses can mount the pavement. This is prevented in many places by very high kerbstones. The bus passengers are jerked about in the process and tempers frayed. Today, I glanced down from the bus window and saw a very old and bedraggled-looking dog; his haunches were perched on the top step of a shop and his front legs were of a convenient length for his paws to meet the step immediately below. He remained impassive; I imagine he has seen this procedure scores of times before. We love the picturesque Old Town and dread what the planners have in store, with their proposal to make a wide road through it. What will be lost? I doubt that we will live to see.

When we disembarked from the bus at the Memorial we saw a young woman wearing the fashion called the New Look, which the newspapers are marvelling over. I could believe it must have been its first appearance in Hastings from the attention its wearer was receiving from passers by. I remarked to Clare that it was delightful to see something so graceful and feminine but the nipped in waist had us both amazed that women should still want to wear beneath a dress whatever it is that creates that illusion; surely, few waists are thus naturally? Ours are a distant memory although neither of us was ever sylph-like. Nowadays, we tend not to be up to the minute with fashion.

I do recall that when attending the wedding of my niece, Sybil Crane in the late 1920s, I wore a very smart cloche hat that was rather too big for me. It kept slipping down my forehead, only stopped in its progress by my spectacles. Clare said that I looked like a mouse peeping out of a hole in the wainscoting so I never wore the hat again. I still have it. Dear Sybil, she has turned out to be a wonderful wife and mother and keeps in regular touch with me.

*

I see that the Hon: Sec: of the Hastings Pig Breeders Association, Mr Rymill, has written to the local newspaper to ask people to stop putting their non-edible waste in the pig food bins. It seems that bottles, tins, rags and paper have been found in the food waste. We do not seem to have public pig waste bins along here and if there were I think they would be unused. We and our neighbours seem to find a use for everything that might be described as waste. Vegetable peelings either go to make compost or to Mrs Todd for her chickens. Clare has a drawer in the kitchen where she stores lengths of string, brown paper and old envelopes, to be used for shopping or reminder lists. I take any bottles and jars for my wine and jam, even though the manufacturers ask us to return them. Clout uses the tins in the garden shed for storing things and mixing paint and other noxious fluids. One can never get enough newspaper. We find it useful for so many things, by the time we have finished it is dirty and beyond salvage.

*

I wonder how visitors to Hastings will manage for rail transport for the season. I saw recently in the paper that there will be fewer trains this summer, to enable coal to be saved for next winter. The government has ordered that there should be 10% fewer trains compared with last summer. They warn the public that this may cause overcrowding on weekend trains and people should try to travel mid-week. This will not be of much use to the working population, who make up the hordes of day-trippers upon whom many seaside businesses depend for their livelihood.

Not that Hastings looks particularly inviting. The bombed sites are cleared of their rubble but there are great gaps in rows of buildings; it's altogether very dreary but I suppose it is the same everywhere. How can reconstruction commence when there are no building materials to spare? Some of the bombed sites are made to look worse by people dumping rubbish on them; I thought that this was against the law.

It was so hot today! When Clare and I arrived home from a visit to a friend in a St Leonard's nursing home, longing for a cup of tea, we found that Edith had left the milk out of the larder and it was on the turn. We had to resort to national dried milk which does not taste good in tea. Clare said that it was not a total loss and she would make some sour milk pancakes.

Sour Milk Pancakes

8 ounces of flour
1 level tsp salt
1 small tsp bicarbonate of soda
Sour milk to mix
Mix together the dry ingredients and then sift
Add the sour milk gradually to make a batter that will drop from the spoon
Ensure that the batter is smooth and without lumps
Drop a large tablespoon of the mixture onto a well-greased griddle or stout frying pan and cook until the edges are cooked, then turn over to brown
Serve with jam or marmalade

*

The daily newspapers are delivered along the Ridge by a local school boy on a ramshackle bicycle. He is a most enterprising child, aged about 10, who does not limit his endeavours to this employment alone. He carries with him his father's ex-army kit bag, offering to householders an ad hoc, fetch and carry service, for a small fee. He also gathers dry sticks as he goes about his round, later bundling them up to sell as kindling. To these, at the appropriate time, he adds the resinous fir cones, good for lighting fires, which fall from the magnificent conifer trees along here.

I am told that the boy's family are the village rag and bone collectors, or scrap merchants, as people tend to say these days, and that although they live in a hovel they are well-off and keep a fortune hidden in their home; I think that this is a common supposition about such people but I believe that that boy will go far. He also helps Clout with gardening jobs. Mrs Smith told me one of the houses to which Clout goes once a week is that of an eccentric lady who never wears day clothes. She walks round the garden, informing Clout of her horticultural requirements, dressed in negligee. It seems that Clout is impervious to her charms but he did ask her not to appear thus in front of the newspaper boy when he worked in the garden. Were it not for Mrs Smith and to a greater degree, Miss Feather, this local tittle-tattle would pass me by. Edith loves it and says it is better than a novel; no harm is done as she quickly forgets most of what she has heard.

*

As well as the controversy about industrial enterprises on the Ridge I see that another even more contentious issue has cropped up in the letters to the Hastings and St Leonards Observer. The prisoners of war, of whom we have quite a number in the locality, are to be allowed to go into Hastings all day Sunday as well as their usual time of Saturday afternoon. A correspondent has suggested this might give an opportunity to local residents to welcome the prisoners into their homes for a meal or a social visit. I am sure there will be an outcry at this suggestion as many people have lost loved ones, homes and businesses to the war and they are not yet ready to forgive.

Occasionally, we see the prisoners in army trucks, passing by from Hollington where some are held, being taken to work on farms. Mrs Smith's son works on a farm at Fairlight. He is big red faced man with very blond hair; the German prisoners call him "komrad" because he looks so Teutonic. He gets on well with them but of course, he came to know so many Germans, ordinary soldiers like himself, while he too was a prisoner of war

*

The government has spent over a quarter of a million pounds on snoek and the Ministry of Food has attempted to increase its appeal by issuing recipes for the fish; pasties, salads, spreads and one for snoek 'piquant-style'. I am told that snoek, soaked in brown sauce, and described as "steak", is served in railway dining cars and British restaurants. Equally unappetising to most people is the whale meat that our butchers are allowed to sell off-ration. We have not tried it for ourselves or James; I am sure he would leave home if presented with it. A neighbour said that whale meat is very tough and even their dog would not eat it but another steeped it in vinegar overnight and then fried it with onions, 'It tasted just like steak', she said. As a patriotic gesture Clare agreed to conjure up something with the snoek that I bought in town a while ago; it was sevenpence a tin. She thought that fish cakes would be a way to turn it into a meal. When she opened the tin a most dreadfully fishy smell wafted out; I had been imaging it would be something like tinned pilchards but it was not. We tried a tiny amount on a fork and we found the flesh to be very tough; Edith would not be tempted. Undaunted, Clare pressed on with her recipe but heating seemed to intensify the horrible fishy flavour and it was altogether very greasy. We tried it on James but after one tentative sniff he walked away with his tail in the air and refused to approach his plate again. He prefers the salt cod, which mercifully, is unrationed. We looked in the encyclopedia to find out about the snoek. It seems it dwells in warm southern waters and is a snake-like fish that hisses like a snake, barks like a dog and has very sharp teeth. It bears a resemblance to the sea serpent of legend. Legendary or not, we asked Clout to bury the fish in the garden. Mrs Smith told us that he took it home to feed to his ferrets; (horrid little things). This unpalatable idea of how to feed the nation is the last straw. While I respect the Food Minister, Sir Stafford Cripps for his fairness in the distribution system of food, his abstemiousness, vegetarianism and austere life, much talked of in the newspaper, he seems to expect the nation to (literally) swallow anything.

Edith said the smell of the snoek had ruined her appetite and that she could only face bread and milk.

Bread and Milk.

Cut a slice of bread into cubes, removing the crusts if wished, (very wasteful)
Place the bread into a small soup bowl
Warm 1/4 pint of milk and pour it over the bread
Sprinkle the mixture with sugar
Serve immediately
Diluted dried milk can be used instead of fresh but it is not as pleasing

*

I spent an interesting evening reading the Riposo vegetarian cookery books, loaned to us by Mrs Pitcairn-Knowles. I was most taken by the old-time advertisements included in the books and to see our favourite Marmite among them, as well as a, "portable bathroom for fifty five shillings." This consisted of an all encompassing folding screen with a circular aperture for the neck. The bather is seated on a chair within the screen along with a container of hot water that provides "a hot air, steam or perfumed bath...invaluable in summer, a necessity in winter". I noted it was recommended for, among other ailments, rheumatism, so it would be welcome in Lavender Cottage. In the recipe section was one for Lettuce a la

Mode. Clare said she has a Ministry of Food recipe for lettuce soup; she is going to try it out next month, when my salad crops are more plentiful (slugs permitting).

Being published in 1928 and 1930 the quantities of eggs and cheese for the Riposo recipes would make them difficult to prepare today but the vegetable dishes are well within possibility. I particularly like Carrots a La Riposo; carrots are a crop that seldom fails me.

Carrots a la Riposo.

2lbs carrots
1/2 a pint of water
1 1/2 ounces of butter, Olnut or Nutter
Salt to taste

Wash and scrape (or peel in winter) the carrots and cut into large julienne pieces
Wash thoroughly again and put onto cook with the fat and water
Stew for one hour (old carrots longer), when there should be some juice left over. This must be thickened with a little flour.
Before serving sprinkle the top with finely chopped parsley.

I do not recall having seen Olnut or Nutter, perhaps they are no longer manufactured. The quantity of butter sounds scandalous in the light of today's ration but of course we would probably cook only half the weight of carrots for our three selves and therefore use less fat. Dripping might be a good substitute for non-vegetarians.

*

I read in the local newspaper that the application to use The Grange for light industry purposes and a hostel has been refused by the council; it was carried by 20 votes to 6. I did not realise that a hostel was part of the plan and it puts rather a different complexion on it. Alderman Ford was reported as saying that it would spoil the green belt to include industry in a residential area. I see that a letter from Miss Winifred Skilton, who is Mrs Todd's neighbour, was part of the front page article. Miss Skilton is great one for knowing what is going on and is said to have 'a heart of gold' when it comes to helping friends and neighbours.

I gleaned from the article that Miss Doris Batty, who is the Headmistress of St Margaret's Boarding School for Girls, near Hurst Court, is also a councillor. I wonder how she gets along with Councillor Mr Symonds, who is known for his somewhat bohemian attitudes. Mrs Smith said that she has a friend, Mrs Hodd, an excellent cook, who used to help out before the war at the Netherwood Guest House kitchen, on special occasions. Mrs Hodd said that Mr Symonds indulged in very "lefty" ideas and unusual behaviour; it seems there was a nudist sunbathing enclosure at Netherwood and a person was employed to keep the prurient at bay.

Visitors to Netherwood from Russia and theatrical people were commonplace before the war. Apparently the gardens were well kept with an indoor gymnasium, a greenhouse for grapes and peaches, even a swimming pool. I am sure that is all gone, as few can afford the upkeep of such extravagances these days. But how we all crave just a little luxury! According to Mrs Smith, Mrs Hodd collects the cream from the top of the milk in a jar and spends hours shaking it, until a small nugget of butter is formed. It made me feel guilty about our parcels from Cousin Marion.

*

It was heartening to read recently that Hastings Mayor has declared open two establishments for the elderly. One, termed a hostel, is a collection of small flats in Holmesdale Gardens and the other an old folks' home in a Georgian mansion called "Old Hastings House", at the northern end of the High Street. It is reported that there are "thirty-two rooms, decorated in keeping with the dignity of the mansion." All this is under the Old People's Welfare Scheme. I am pleased that our generation is not forgotten in the clamour for new dwellings.

We had a real treat today. A fisherman came up from the Old Town with a handcart laden with basketsful of fresh mackerel. He told us that at this time of the year huge shoals of mackerel drive the sprats into the shallows so that they can feast on them. The mackerel are in such numbers and so intent on catching their prey they lose all sense of caution and can be picked up in the hands of anyone who walks into the sea. (So that is where the saying a "sprat to catch a mackerel" comes from). The mackerel were only tuppence each and we would have liked to buy a good quantity but have no means of preserving them; it is such hot weather at present. They are a handsome fish and the flesh is so meaty, full of flavour and nourishment; infinitely more palatable than the ghastly snoek. I did not expect cooking advice from a fisherman but come to think of it, who is more likely to know how to cook fish? He advised against the sousing method (poaching the mackerel in a mixture of vinegar and water with herbs or spices), 'ruins it', he said; telling us frying the flour-coated fish and eating it with bread or potatoes is much better. While this conversation took place James, swaying slightly, gazed at the fisherman as if mesmerised; three more cats slunk about the handcart. They must have found the fishy aroma intoxicating. We bought seven mackerel, hoping that if we cooked them all today the leftover fish could be eaten cold tomorrow with salad. The odd fish is for James and no doubt it will be my job to pick out all the bones for him. But mackerel are easier to fillet than herring.

July

We were favored with unbroken sunshine yesterday and the garden party was a resounding success. Church and other friends, neighbours and even passers by thronged our garden. Clout came in on Friday to trim the grass verges and tidy both the front and back gardens. The delphiniums and lupins were giving of their best and the pink rambling roses made a perfect arbour for the outdoor "tea room." We were most fortunate in the matter of the generous donations of bric-a-brac and so were able to have a white elephant stall. Quite literally, in fact, as a neighbour whose late husband had served in India, gave us a number of small ivory elephants. As a job lot these raised five shillings! Thanks to the heat wave the garden produce stall was groaning; new potatoes, lettuce and fresh flowers were the first to be sold. Riposo was very forthcoming with vegetables. Mrs Pitcairn-Knowles sent a big basketful over, saying they had a glut. They were brought by her son, aged about 14 or 15; I think his name is Richard. He is a tall, good looking boy with a gentle demeanour. Edith believes his nature is due to being a life-long vegetarian, as she is. If it is true, as she is convinced it is, that a lack of meat breeds gentle people and if the nation's rations of meat do not increase soon, we will be raising a generation of angels! Mrs Todd, who keeps hens, gave us four new laid eggs in a pretty, handmade raffia basket for the produce stall.

The teas were very popular: The bread rationing scheme has settled down and seems almost non-existent at times; a kind word to the baker usually produces an extra loaf or two. Clare made sandwiches, filled with anything she could get. The lettuce and Marmite variety was surprisingly popular; the Marmite concealing the scarcity of margarine. As always, there was spam, enlivened with some of my apple chutney from last autumn. Clare made jam buns and rock cakes; their being served slightly warmed made up for the absence of any great quantity of fat or dried fruit in the mixture. There were strawberries for tea, (tuppence extra), and Clare whisked up a tin of the Canadian evaporated milk, which passed as cream. Mrs Smith came up with a tip for washing the strawberries that was surprisingly efficient. A little vinegar added to the rinse water brought forth an absolute zoo of creatures and I wondered now many of these we had innocently consumed in the past.

We were all astounded at Mrs Todd offering to exhibit her parrot, Laura, at the garden party. She is used to being outside in Mrs Todd's back garden so it was no hardship to the bird. She sat in her cage behind a screen and for a halfpenny children could have a glimpse of her. Early in the procedure Laura gave forth with "Damn Yer," her favourite ejaculation, much to the delight of the small boy whose turn it was to view her. This excitement drew a queue of children but Laura uttered not one more word and was banished from the garden after she attempted to bite a child who intruded a finger into the cage. Alas, the afternoon did not bring forth a smile from Mrs Todd but Laura raised one shilling and tuppence. Her owner's hackles were also raised, when she overheard a remark about "a cantankerous old bird" and thought it referred to her. People began to drift away at about five o'clock but it was still so hot we did not start to clear the garden until after seven; a few kind neighbours came back to lend a hand.

We sat in the garden afterwards till quite late, enjoying the blessed coolness and the scent of roses and honeysuckle. Edith was exhausted with heat and excitement and fell asleep in her deck chair. She had enjoyed the day so much and was quite her old self. (Her maid had searched out one of Edith's pre-war garden party gowns and hats, making her the belle of the occasion. Clare and I remained in overalls all day, myself resplendent in a new one; its first outing. Clare served the teas with the help of Miss Feather and I moved from stall to stall, tempting pennies out of purses. There were 321 peas in the jar; I was the one who had counted them in the day before).

As dusk fell Clare and I had a glass of my parsnip wine and a few cigarettes, to discourage the mosquitoes. I noted, as I viewed my crops from a deck chair, that Clout's tip about casting handfuls of dusty soil on the runner bean vines has kept the aphids at bay. I asked him, in jocular mode, if it worked because when the dust got in the eyes of the aphids they had to rub them, thus letting go of the bean plant and falling off; he gave me a withering look. He explained aphids are clean insects so hate anything dirty. His tip about watering the soil around the young cabbage plants with a weak dilution of Jeyes Fluid, when the first white butterflies appear, has been very effective. There is not a pest to be seen on the cabbages. Clout said that the plants take up the fluid and it scents them enough to keep the pests at bay but not enough to affect the flavour to human taste. I have not let Edith into this secret for fear that she will say the cabbage tastes of disinfectant!

James, who had been asleep on my bed during the garden party, chased imaginary mice in the bushes. For all his considerable age he's very energetic at times. On going indoors we counted our takings and found that our happy and successful day had brought in nearly six pounds. It all reminded me of the fund-raising summer garden parties we used to give for the church in the years before the war. I think the last one we held was in July 1939.

Rock Cakes and Jam Buns.

The two different cakes can be made from one basic recipe. These are always popular and are so easy to make.

8 ounces of flour
3 ounces of sugar
1/2 teaspoon spice
A little milk
1 reconstituted egg or one fresh egg
4 ounces of fat, which could be mixed; dripping, cooking fat or margarine
3 ounces of whatever dried fruit is to hand
1 teaspoon baking powder and a pinch of salt

Sieve all dry ingredients together and then rub in the fat until the mixture is like very fine breadcrumbs
Then add the egg blended with the milk to make a very stiff mixture
Lastly, add the dried fruit
Put mixture in rough heaps on a greased baking tin and cook in a rather quick oven for 20-25 minutes.

For jam buns; leave out the dried fruit
Place a heap of the plain mixture on to a baking tray
Make a dip in the centre of each bun with a floured finger tip and spoon in a little jam. (Raspberry or strawberry the are the best)
Bake as for rock cakes.

Apple Chutney

8 ounces of onions, grated or finely chopped
1/2 pint of malt vinegar

2 pounds of peeled, chopped apples
1/2 teaspoon of pickling spice
1 teaspoon of salt
1 teaspoon of ground ginger
12 ounces of sugar
2 to 4 ounces of dried fruit. A few dates or prunes could make up the weight.

Put the onions into the saucepan with a little of the vinegar and cook gently until nearly soft
Add the apples, salt, ground ginger and the spices, which should be tied in a piece of clean cloth, so that they can be easily removed
Cook on a low heat, stirring all the time until the mixture is soft
Add the rest of the vinegar and stir in well with the sugar and dried fruit. Boil steadily until the chutney thickens
Take out the spices and pour the hot chutney into warmed jars and seal at once
If the jars have metal caps put thick paper or card on the top of the chutney to prevent rust spoiling it

Parsnip Wine
12 large parsnips
8 cups sugar
1 gallon water
1 orange
1 lemon
1 tablespoon yeast
1 slice of toast

Wash but do not peel the parsnips
Cut into slices and place in a saucepan with the water
Cook until tender
Strain the liquid into a bowl with the sugar, orange and lemon Stir until the sugar is dissolved, then place the warm toast on top with the yeast spread on it
Leave for 10 days or so before straining and bottling
Cork tightly for eight weeks and keep for 6 months before using.

This wine is very strong and should be treated with respect. Its colour when mature is very like that of whiskey. It is best made in February or March with parsnips which have remained in the ground all the winter. No problem this year!

*

Clare made lettuce soup yesterday. This may sound a somewhat bland dish but it certainly was not. The recipe produced about one and half pints of soup, which we had for lunch. Edith went quite mad on it and consumed three platefuls; soon after lunch was over she fell into a deep sleep on the sofa. I had to go out to our little shop nearby and I mentioned in passing to the proprietor, Mr Watson, the new soup recipe and Edith's falling so deeply asleep. He, fount of all knowledge, said he had read that lettuce contains laudanum and perhaps that was why Edith was so sleepy. As it was, she slept right through the afternoon, waking only to join us at supper, and then going to bed very early. She was none the worse next morning and said how refreshed she felt.

Lettuce, parsley and potato soup

1 medium onion
2 medium potatoes cut into thick slices
2 lettuces
A bunch of parsley
1 and a half pints vegetable stock
Salt and pepper
2 tablespoons dripping or some other fat

Chop the onion and fry in fat until soft
Add the potato and cook gently for a further 3 minutes
Add the stock and simmer for 10 minutes
Add the chopped lettuce and parsley and continue simmering until all ingredients are completely cooked
Sieve soup and season to taste with salt and pepper.

*

The appointed day of the performance of "Boy Wanted" came round so quickly, as everything seems to when one is old. I was invited to take a companion to the school to see the event. Clare said she would like to come so Miss Feather offered to sit with Edith to keep her company and be the first to hear how it all went. I thought I should make some effort with my dress so the make-do-and-mend navy blue coat was pressed into service; Clare's best beige straw hat and gloves completed the ensemble. She felt that there was no need for her to shine sartorially as she was not the guest of honour.

Again the car was sent and on our arrival the headmaster, Mr Curtis, was waiting to greet us in the vestibule of the school and to escort us to our seats. The school's assembly hall was set up as a theatre; there was no stage but a long, low podium served as such. There was a hum of interest when we entered the hall but I fear the boys were disappointed to find the author so elderly and not at all glamorous. Our seats were in the front row, of course. The headmaster said a few words about the play, adding that, 'The author is honouring us with her presence this evening.'

The star, to my mind, was the boy who played Aunt Maria. I understand that the boys hate playing female parts but this character is so dominant she probably does not seem particularly feminine. I think the boy who took the part must at some time have seen the Brandon Thomas's play "Charley's Aunt", as he brought the gusto required for the title role to his interpretation. The boys had clearly worked very hard to create a Victorian clerical office out of a few items of old furniture and random props. The entrances of the Perfectly Perfect Boy and the Demon King were heralded, as the script dictates, by a loud bang. This was achieved by the use of a tin tray and a rolling pin and had the effect of greatly startling the audience, as I had intended. The pupil who played the Lively Boy had some difficulty with the required Irish accent, wandering into Wales at times, but nobody seemed to be troubled by it. It was the most wonderful experience to see one's ideas and words brought to life by actors, albeit youthful amateurs. After the finale there were several "curtain calls", (in fact the curtains were the screens from the school sanatorium), followed by much applause and a "Hip, Hip Hurrah" for the author. The boys asked me to sign their home made programmes and "Aunt Maria" presented me with a large bouquet of garden roses.

I was driven home in a daze, leaving it to Clare to regale Edith and Miss Feather with the details of a most entertaining evening. How gossip gets around among the neighbours! Next day several people called, on the vaguest pretexts, in truth to find out what had been going on. Rumour had it that I had written a play that was to be produced on the wireless and I was set to become renowned! This sounds very like the exaggerated gossip that might be purveyed by Miss Feather's part-time maid, who works in the kitchens at Hurst Court.

*

It was fortunate for us that we held our garden party early in the month. There was a dramatic change in the weather on the 17th. Between about 12.30am and 4.00am, we had the most dreadful thunderstorm. The rain was torrential and such lightning and thunder! Edith was very frightened and none of us could sleep. So Clare made some cocoa and I coaxed James from under my bed and we took turns in soothing him on our laps, till the storm abated.   We read in the Hastings and St Leonards Observer today that the chimney stack of Mr Henson's Stores at Baldslow was struck by lightning. At the time Mr Henson was working in the telephone exchange, attached to the stores, and the fuses of the equipment blew. Mr Henson was not harmed but the National Fire Service was working until 2.15am to make things safe.

There was flooding in Hastings Town Centre as the drains could not cope with the volume of water. There was a picture of the damage to a lady's sitting room, with a tide-mark half way up the wall. It must have ruined everything, including the piano in the photograph. I hope she gets some help to replace her furniture, but where will it come from in these austere times? The Women's Voluntary Service have turned to with generous supplies of cleaning materials; such a splendid organisation, in war and peacetime.

*

I had planned to pick the last of the soft fruit for jam making now that the garden has dried out after this long spell of rain. Mrs Todd had given me a few more jars and my and Clare's going without sugar in most things meant I had some by me. But I have had to take to my bed as I do not feel well; I cannot write more now.

August

I have not been able to write letters or my journal for some time. At the end of July I was stricken with a bout of pneumonia, just as I was last year. I have been confined to bed ever since and it has fallen to Clare to be my nurse. Had she not been up to the job I would surely have been sent to hospital. She also had to keep an eye on Edith who, responding to the disturbed state of domestic affairs, suffered more frequent spells of wandering, in body and mind. This put her in need of constant attention and reassurance, an extra burden on Clare, when she is so hard pressed.

*

Our doctor was very good and visited me as often as he could. He is getting on in years now and most of the work is done by his son but the father likes to keep up with his old patients. He is a wonderfully compassionate man; somebody told me he was a surgeon in the trenches in the Great War and was wounded in 1917. He has a pronounced limp but one has learned not to ask... He treated the pneumonia with M and B, which people are now calling penicillin; it shortened the most serious phase of the illness but the cough and pain in the lungs were very testing at times. The doctor said that I should give up smoking; not that I could smoke when I was ill. Medical men seem for ever contradicting themselves; during the war we were encouraged to smoke, 'Good for the nerves,' the doctors said.

*

Mrs Smith said that the town was crowded during the August Bank Holiday. She and her family went to the beach and there was hardly a space to sit, as the tide was in. They had a terrible fright when her little grandson disappeared among the throng but he was soon found, seated in front of a Punch and Judy show. Speaking of shows; Edith had a particularly good day recently when she unearthed something she had kept since her childhood; a Pollock's Toy Theatre, made of paper and wood. I recall that they were popular in the 1880s and provided great entertainment, with characters and scenery printed on sheets of paper, ready to cut out and slot into little metal stands, in order to move them across the stage. Edith insisted on setting it all up on my bed and guiding the little figures through a complete production, reading the script and singing the songs. I must confess I fell asleep for a while but Edith was so absorbed that she did not seem to notice. It gave her a happy interlude and Clare some time to catch up on the household accounts. How well she keeps them, I wish I had her head for figures but I am like father. He had no notion of how to manage money and always seemed to be on the brink of penury. The relatives were so good to him but this is the way in our family. Cousin Marion is exemplary in this respect with the parcels she sends us.

*

There was nothing cheerful from the Prime Minister, Mr Atlee, when he spoke on the wireless recently. He appealed for a wartime-style national effort to tackle the country's economic crisis, saying he had no easy words to offer and that he could not say when the nation would emerge into better times. It's very discouraging, just lying here, when there is so much to be done in the garden in the way of harvesting and tidying. Clout has given us an extra half day and Clare is in an absolute whirl of activity; gathering and salting down runner beans and bottling tomatoes. Thank goodness I was well when the soft fruit burgeoned or we would have no jam next year.

*

It was Clare's 76th birthday this week. Fortunately, I had ordered a book of poetry for her from Mason's in Bohemia Road some weeks ago, otherwise, being bed-bound, I would have had nothing to give her to mark the occasion. Mason's are a very good book shop; they conducted the business most efficiently, via post and telephone calls. I recommend them most thoroughly. Clare was delighted that I had thought of her birthday and kissed my cheek and said, 'Thank you, my dear Emilie,' which was very touching, as she is not given to demonstrations of affection. She then quickly went about her duties with her usual briskness.

*

Days can seem very long when one is confined to bed. Mrs Todd is so good with practical help and bedside visits. While I have a little grumble, she sits with me in tranquil near-silence, uttering the occasional and soothing, 'dear me', and exuding a faintly curry-like odour. Clare tells me this smell is Karswood Spice, which Mrs Todd adds to the hot mash that she cooks up for her chickens, the spice encourages the birds to lay and gives the eggs richer yolks. As a result of many years of storing Karswood spice indoors and regularly cooking it up, the smell has permeated her house and everything in it; it is not unpleasant.

Miss Feather looks in every day with a book, flowers or some magazine or the other. There is always the newspaper to provide distraction. Not that it takes long to read as the restriction on newsprint is very stringent. I find myself dwelling on the obituaries and becoming unhealthily introspective.

*

I am occasionally assailed by sounds of the outside world: In the holidays the local boys play cricket on the Hurst Court sports field and I can hear the sound of leather on willow and triumphant shouts. On fine days the residents of Riposo across the road play croquet; I had no idea that it was such a riotous game, stimulating yells of glee.

All-in-all the Ridge is mostly quiet; not much traffic in the day, apart from the buses, which, being trolleys, are very quiet. The old tram tracks beneath the road surface were torn up for scrap early in the war and the Ridge was never properly repaired afterwards; the road is still in a bad condition and almost as uneven as a country lane in some places. There is a particularly rough patch on the road outside the cottage which, when hit by a trolley bus or a heavy vehicle, results in a loud thump; it punctuates my long days. There are many actual lanes that lead down from the Ridge. Some are un-surfaced and in the spring their hedgerows and the nearby woods are full of bluebells, primroses, anemones and violets. But oh, the mud in winter! We used to walk there often. Will I become well enough to do so once more, I wonder? What a grump I am, to be sure.

*

Edith was most insistent that she should listen to a programme called "Down Your Way" on our wireless. (I do wish she would get one of her own, her private income is quite good and she could easily afford it). It seems that Richard Dimbleby tours the country, visiting different towns to talk to selected inhabitants; it is the turn of Hastings this week. After speaking, the person can have music of their choice played. This is where the problem arises: One is at the mercy of the taste of each individual and you can depend on there being a crooner or two in the choice but it had to be endured in case Edith missed the talking part. Clare says that crooning is groaning set to music and that sort of music hardly merits the word.

*

I feel so tired and cannot write properly just now. I must ask Clare to send a card to Cousin Marion to apologise for my failure to reply to her last letter, to tell her I have been unwell, but not to make too much of it. I do not want to be the cause of worry.

*

Such an interesting piece in the local newspaper last week: A local resident, a Mr F Leslie Crew, who is the President of the Association of Round Tables of the British Isles, made a visit by air to America and Canada. He was determined not to talk about food during his visit. (How well I understand that, none of us can keep off the topic these days)! Mr Crew was very impressed with what he saw in the way of shops and goods in America and the general abundance of everything. In Canada he attended a convention where, contrary to his original intention, he was asked to talk about food and display an example of the typical week's ration allocated to a British person. The conference delegates were shocked at the meagre portions on which we have to live. People immediately wanted to help; those who had no British relatives asked Mr Crew for the addresses of strangers, so that they could send food parcels to a family in 'the Old Country.' It made me realise once again how fortunate we are to be the recipients of Cousin Marion's generosity.

*

This hot, dry August has resulted in a marvellous wheat crop around here. The German prisoners of war have been working with our Land Army girls to bring in the harvest. Mrs Smith tells me that a girl from her village has struck up a particular friendship with one of the prisoners and is the object of disapproval as a result. While I was suffering most severely from the effects of the pneumonia, Double Summer Time came to an end, I think it was on the 10th August; we thereafter reverted to Summer Time until November.

September

Our Church Minister, Mr Hilton, called this morning to ask after Edith as she has been ill. He must grow tired of visiting Lavender Cottage coming as often as he did when I had the pneumonia. He lives in Hoadswood Road and walks here, as he says, 'To save petrol, and improve my health.' What with one thing and another we have not been to church for weeks. Mr Hilton brought us some Victoria plums from his garden. Mrs Smith was just making tea and so he was pleased to join me; Clare had gone to the library. The mid-morning sunshine was glorious so we settled in the front sitting room. Meanwhile, Mrs Smith fussed around in the hallway outside. Thursday is her morning for cleaning the sitting room and she was somewhat put out at her routine being disrupted.

Last week we found some rags for Mrs Smith to cut up for use as dusters. Among the discarded items were Edith's pink, much-darned cotton drawers. As the Minister made his goodbyes to me in the hallway Mrs Smith was energetically polishing the banisters with what was obviously the pink undergarment that she had not bothered to dismember. He must think this is a mad household. I did not tell Clare about the dusting incident when she returned. She gets so cross with Mrs Smith at times about not keeping up appearances; she, in return, always defends herself forthrightly. I find conflict so upsetting. Clare was very pleased with the plums; they were soft and juicy and needed no sugar. We received some suet in our delivery from the butcher yesterday, a rare treat, so we had plum pudding. The scent of it brought Edith from her sick bed to the top of the stairs to call out an enquiry as to whether plums are a food fit for invalids; she was disappointed at being told they are not and that a dish of junket awaited her attention.

Basic Suet Pastry

8 ounces of flour
3-4 ounce finely grated suet
I teaspoon of baking powder
Pinch of salt
Cold water to mix

Mix together the flour, suet, salt and baking powder. Add enough cold water to make a soft paste but stiff enough to roll out.

Plum Pudding

Cut off about 3/4 of the suet pastry roll it out and use it to line a pudding basin which has been lightly greased
Fill the basin with the fruit and add water if necessary and as much sugar as you can spare, if the fruit is sour
You can use saccharine but it has a metallic taste
With the remainder of the pastry make a lid and press the edges together
Put a greased paper on the pudding surface and cover the pudding with a cloth made from clean pieces of rag and tie it with string.

(We have some squares of old sheeting which we have washed and used repeatedly for this purpose).

Lower the pudding into a pot of boiling water but do not allow the water to cover the pudding
Gently boil it for two to two and a half hours, replenishing the boiling water as needed
Lift the pudding out by the string and uncover the pudding carefully as it will be very hot
Serve with packet custard made with dried milk

Junket

1/2 pint of milk
1 lump of sugar
1/2 teaspoon of rennet
Grated nutmeg

Warm the milk with sugar to blood heat
Pour into dish and add rennet
Leave in a warm place until set
Grate nutmeg over the surface of the junket when set.
This makes two portions of junket

*

Miss Feather came to see us yesterday in a state of great distress. She had received a letter from the Methodist Church Authorities informing her that a new minister has been appointed and she will have to vacate "Claremont" by 31st January 1948. The letter also said that, as the elderly dependent of a minister, she would be entitled to a place in an establishment, near London, run by the church and a bed sitting-room would be available to her. All Miss Feather could say was. 'What about Nanki-Poo?' (He is her Pekingese dog). It seems no pets are allowed in the home. Well, of course, we cannot take him; James would never tolerate it and the ever helpful Mrs Todd has her parrot, which would probably terrorise the dog. There is also the duty of walking the poor little thing three times a day, not arduous, as he is too old to go far, but very time consuming. Miss Feather enjoys these little forays as it gives her an opportunity to catch up on gossip. How she will miss all that and we her kindness and chatty visits.

Miss Feather kept coming in to talk to us throughout the day, as different aspects of moving came to her mind, saying, 'What about all that heavy furniture, how will I dispose of it? And, 'What shall I do with all the books and pictures?' She can only take a few personal things as the room at the establishment is already furnished and there is only one cupboard. Circumstances can be very cruel to the elderly spinster. Miss Feather has devoted her life to her father and the church; her much older siblings are dead and the nieces and nephews are far flung and rarely visit. If only she could get accommodation in Hastings House but I fear that the fact a place has already been offered to her elsewhere means that she has no hope in that quarter. And there is probably a waiting list, as with most things now.

*

I wonder if "Claremont" will undergo any repairs and decorations before the new minister moves in. I read that when it comes to building work these days permits are required for almost everything. To add to the delays, the forms to apply for the permits are often not available. Lavender Cottage is in need of outside repairs and much interior redecoration. We did have new glass in the windows after the doodlebug landed in the woods at the back of the cottage and our rear windows were blown out. How fortunate for us that we were all out at the time. The cottage interior has had to make do with my efforts with the distemper brush. Good paint and wallpaper are difficult to find at present. Public buildings look very shabby both inside and out. I noticed when I was at Hurst Court in July that the place looked very dreary, not that the boys mind, I am sure. It is a grand building; its solid, grey stone walls make it look like a seminary. I believe it has a connection with the Jesuits, who occupied it for some years. The building looks as if it will stand for centuries.

*

The weather continues fine and dry and it is hard to believe the summer is over. Clare is reluctant to clear the annuals from the front garden as they continue to flower vigorously. It is pleasant to look out on the colour and Edith likes to gather and arrange little posies for her room. I do not feel strong enough yet to do any real gardening so it will probably be Clout's task to tidy up for autumn. The potato crop is very good and the runner beans have been prolific this year, probably benefiting from the spell of heavy rain in mid-July. I helped Clare salt down a batch of runner beans this afternoon. It is a restful job as one can do it sitting down.

Salting Down Runner Beans.

One pound of salt is required for every three pounds of runner beans
Ceramic jars are best for salting
The beans should be washed and the stalks, strings and any bad spots removed
The beans can be sliced lengthways or cut into two inch pieces
Put a layer of salt then a layer of beans, alternating until the jar is filled to inch below the top
The ratio is about 4 ounces of salt to one layer of beans
Store the filled jar, covered and in a cool place
The convenience of salting is that the jar does not have to be filled at one time, but can be added to over several days, as the crop becomes ready
To use the beans soak them in cold water until the salt is removed then cook as usual

We have had our salting jars for years. They belonged to Clare's grandmother, who was a Kent market gardener's wife, famous for her preserves and pickles.

*

I noticed in the local newspaper that an official party of visitors has arrived in Hastings, from Dordrecht in Holland. It seems that they have been made very welcome by the townspeople and civic bodies. I recall that last year a member of our church made her first visit to her family in Holland and France since before the war. She was shocked at the hardship and deprivation she found there. On her return she gave us a talk on the subject to our Church Women's League, who sent a parcel of clothing to Holland. As much as we complain about conditions here we were not occupied by an invading army, our people subjugated and murdered in the streets. Soldiers of the British occupying forces on leave from Germany tell stories of the terrible state of that country. Much as I condemn the war I cannot but feel pity for the German people, especially the children and the elderly folk.

*

I felt sad to discover, being unable to attend, that the civic opening of the Municipal concert season will take place at the end of the month, with a performance by the Southern Philharmonic Orchestra. They are playing a programme of our particular favourites. The seats are not too expensive, unreserved being two shillings, but as usual it is the transport that poses the difficultly. Perhaps before the season ends we can have a car to go to one performance. I also saw that Harold McMillan MP came to Hastings to speak at the Conservative Party HQ. I am not a Conservative but I would have liked to have heard what he had to say. There is something statesman-like and dignified about his appearance; I wonder if it is matched by his oratory.

October

We finally persuaded Edith to see her solicitor in order to change her will. She has promised to do this so often in order to put Clare and me on a proper legal footing regarding the cottage, should she go before us. It was only the inducement of tea at the Creamery in Robertson Street that moved Edith to put on her things and get into the taxi. Edith dislikes dealing with any kind of business; I don't know where we would be without Clare's kindly but determined management. The Creamery was looking shabby, especially the carpets and the tea was inferior. Edith made short work of the cakes, even though their attractive appearance camouflaged very dry and tasteless confections. So different from the dear old Valdelo of pre-war days; their afternoon teas, accompanied by a string quartet, were a delight.

When we left the Creamery a gale was coming in off the sea and roaring down Robertson Street like a steam train. Edith could hardly stand and became upset, saying that she would never be able to walk to her solicitor's office even though it is close by, in the seafront Palace Chambers. We went back inside the tea room and tried to calm Edith and tidy her and ourselves. It was then Edith discovered that she had left her handbag in the car we had taken to Hastings. Clare asked if she could use the Creamery's telephone to call the driver, who said he had the handbag in his safekeeping. By then Edith was weeping, I do not know if was about her bag or because one of her scarves had been carried away by the wind. Any notion of her being up to dealing with the solicitor was quite out of the question. Clare asked the driver to collect us as soon as possible so that we could return home. She then telephoned the solicitor to apologise for Edith not keeping her appointment.

We had another pot of the dreadful tea while we waited. When we arrived home Edith went straight to bed, saying that she was certain to have caught a chill, as indeed she probably has, considering that she was set on it being so. Dear stalwart Clare quickly made a decent pot of tea while I stirred the fire into life. For supper Clare fried the kippers that she had bought in town; James went completely mad during the cooking process, weaving himself round her ankles till he almost tripped her up. Gale or no gale he had to go outside. Edith called down asking us to shut the kitchen door, as the smell of the fish was rising up the stairs and making her feel faint, and could she have some bread and milk.

At times Clare and I feel that we have the care of a spoilt child. This is how Edith's long-suffering mother treated her until she died in 1931 and we have inherited the responsibility. It's such a pity we did not settle this will business but no doubt things will work out satisfactorily in the end. We let James in and he was very cross and windswept; he looked like a flu brush and spurned offers of the tastiest morsels of kipper. We have two spoilt children!

*

We were thrilled to receive a parcel from Cousin Marion containing a gorgeous box of toilet soap and packets of Sunlight household soap, which we have not seen for ages. As for the Lux Soap Flakes therein; well, I believe we did have a packet a year ago. In any case we haven't seen any good soap for many months so it was all wonderfully welcome. What a quantity it is, we shall certainly be clean for a twelvemonth. The parcel was so well packed that the dried eggs, butter and fats had not picked up the scent of the soap. The tinned strawberries and peach jam will be a great treat.

*

I had to cancel a talk last week to the church literary society on The Human Face by John Brophy. This is the second time I have done so this year; they will cease to take my offers seriously if I keep letting them down. I feel I am a nuisance being in bed at present but Clare makes no trouble of it. Our young doctor was not very cheerful when he called as he was starting an illness, adding that his father has pneumonia badly. It seems to be a widespread complaint here; they say that the drought is causing much illness. Things are pretty restless all round; it would not surprise me if another election arrived before its time. Many people, who voted for the Labour party, expecting them to perform miracles to advance the country's recovery, have been disappointed. But I think it would have been the same whoever was in government. It's difficult for me to write just now; perhaps I will be better soon and not so addle-headed. I did not expect to have so much illness this year or that it would interfere with my journal writing as it has.

*

To our surprise the grocer included a knuckle of smoked bacon, priced tuppence, in our delivery this week; being mostly bone the knuckle was off-ration. Although it can be described as not being much more than a pig's wrist it had the potential to provide several meals. Clare soaked the knuckle in cold water overnight to remove the salt, and then boiled it for an hour. She took the knuckle from the water, which she allowed to go cold. She skimmed off most of the fat and set it aside for frying purposes. To the bacon water Clare added a chopped onion, a carrot, a potato, sage and thyme from the garden and let it simmer for an hour. This, thickened with flour, produced a tasty and warming soup. So many foods are bland these days, due to the lack of fat, so the bacon-fatty stock was a treat.

Clare removed the knuckle skin and hung it in a tree for the birds; they went mad on it! She minced the few ounces of meat on the bone with an onion, bread crumbs and sage, adding reconstituted dried egg to the mixture, which was formed into rissoles and fried in the reclaimed bacon fat. With potatoes and cabbage these made an excellent meal. Our frugality would not allow us to discard the bone until it had one more boiling, the stock from this making some lentil soup; a little Symington's soup powder and Marmite added extra flavour. This parsimonious tale sounds almost Dickensian, more so when it concluded with the bone going across to Laura the parrot, who must have been hard put to it to find anything other than diversion in this scrap.

*

Yesterday we heard of a rescue carried out by our milk delivery girl. Miss Feather picked up the story while out with Nanki-Poo; the dog-walking folk round here are a regular clan! It seems Joyce called for payment from two elderly ladies who live alone in a large house along here. They were in a very distressed state and in urgent need of a veterinary surgeon, as their little dog had a bone wedged across the roof of his mouth. The poor creature was crazed with pain, if one could judge by the noise it was making and its wild behaviour. Joyce could not provide the name of a vet but saw that something needed to be done at once. So she grasped the dog between her knees, forced his mouth open and carefully pulled out the bone, suffering two bitten fingers in the process. The ladies were extremely grateful. As Joyce would not take any money they insisted she accept a bag of sugar instead.

*

We had a surprise visit from the young people in my family on Saturday. Somehow they had got hold of a supply of petrol and had come on a run down to the coast, incorporating a visit to this aged aunt in the process. They had prepared a picnic, which they shared with us. How delightful it is to entertain when the guests bring their own banquet; and such treats! I did hint at wishing to know from whence this bounty came, being concerned about the black market. There was a touching of noses, added to the remark that, 'they knew somebody who had an American boyfriend.' Deciding to view this unexpected largesse as being in the same category as Cousin Marion's parcels, we set about enjoying every morsel. To praise a few items; the cheese, (such a great lump) chocolate cake and tinned peaches were delicious. Edith joined in quite merrily; she is a terror for sweet things and the company did her so much good.

When the young people heard of the fix were are in for transport, one offered to come down next spring, if we could find them a bed for the night, and take me out to tea and in the evening, to a performance of the Municipal Orchestra, before their season ends. It was a thrilling offer. I accepted pro tem (I trust they will include Clare), hoping that when the time comes all will be well with us and the weather.

*

This has been a week of surprise visitors: Yesterday afternoon two boys from Hurst Court came as emissaries of their headmaster. 'Would Miss Crane kindly accept Mr Curtis' compliments and a copy of the school's summer term magazine?' A report on the performance of "Boy Wanted" was included in the pages, along with a not very clear photograph of the cast. (This is not a criticism, with such inferior paper and printing facilities these days what can one expect)? The boys declined the offer of cake and tea, saying they had to get back to do prep. One said, on leaving and spotting James on the windowsill, 'I say, Miss Crane, what a splendid cat, is he yours?' (It made me wonder to whom James actually belongs; deciding later that we all three belong to him)! I enjoyed the youthful enthusiasm with which the play was reviewed in the magazine and the writer's view of the plot, so different from mine. No matter, that is the way with all literature, even my own humble efforts.

*

Miss Feather called to see us on Wednesday evening. The ladies from her church had been to see a matinee of the Hastleon's production of The Gondoliers and she had just got home and was longing to tell somebody about the marvellous performance. She said that she is very fond of Gilbert and Sullivan, her favourite being the Mikado, hence her dog being named Nanki-Poo, after the operetta's hero. This mention of her dog brought her back to the problem of what to do about him when she moves. People are reluctant to take on an elderly dog because it may become sick. And where do people find food for the poor dogs these days? So-called "scraps for the dog" are a distant memory in most peoples' homes.

November

For the first time since before the war there were public Guy Fawkes Celebrations. Not that at our age we felt any urge to participate, but a measure of involvement was thrust upon us in the person of small boys in the village, trundling around Guys in wooden carts, whilst chanting "Penny for the Guy"; not a 'please' to be heard. I did not give; to do so invites the boys in swarms. This year, Hydnye House Boys School had a great bonfire; you could see the glow in the sky from here, such a waste of combustible material, when we are all struggling to get fuel. They also had fireworks, some very loud, which frightened James to such a degree that he hid under my bed, as he used to do during air raids.

Edith was also upset and thought the war was still on and I admit it also gave me that feeling. I believe that in our minds we will never get over the war. I think the time in 1940 when the German aircraft crashed in the field close to us was the most terrible thing but the flying bombs passing over the Ridge struck fear into us all. Mrs Smith said that her grandchildren were wild with delight at the Guy Fawkes procession in the village; the little ones had never seen such a sight. A gigantic elaborately dressed Guy was fixed to the back of a lorry and driven round the village, accompanied by a fancy-dressed entourage. There was a picture of it in the local paper but it was so small it was impossible to see any real details.

*

We listened to the Royal Wedding on the wireless. The music was beautiful but it felt intrusive to hear so clearly the couple making their vows. Our friends have been at odds with each other about this part of the event, some saying it is unseemly for the world to be privy to a sacred and personal rite. Others think that the money spent on a lavish public spectacle is out of place, when we are struggling with poor rations and shortages of so many things, but it seems to have cheered up some people. Mrs Smith was invited to see the day's events on a television in the home of one of the better-off families for whom she works. We will be interested to hear her opinion of the transmission.

*

When I asked Mrs Smith about the Royal Wedding on the television she muttered, 'the least said about that the better.' I held my tongue, knowing that the full story would follow later. As Mrs Smith got round to cleaning the cooker, a job she dislikes, she held forth to Clare, who was preparing vegetables.

She said that when she arrived to see the Royal Wedding she found the drawing room packed with the family's well-off friends and relations, including their very "uppity" married daughter. She immediately told Mrs Smith to make tea and coffee for everyone. Believing that she was also a guest, Mrs Smith was taken aback but she did not want to make a scene so she complied. And this was how the day continued, with Mrs Smith making sandwiches, serving cakes, clearing away and washing up; even giving a bottle to and changing a nappy for a baby that belonged to a complete stranger. I asked her if she saw the Royal Wedding and she said, 'Just a bit here and there Miss Crane, but only from the drawing room door, I was never asked to sit down. I thought I'd been mistaken about being a guest so waited till the end to be paid. But when everyone had gone and I had cleared up and washed up for the umpteenth time, the missus came to the kitchen and said that she hoped I had enjoyed it, never a purse or penny in sight. So I said no I didn't enjoy it missus, you got me here on false pretences and you either pay me for me services or that's it for you and me. She said how dare you, so I just got me coat and walked out. I was getting fed up with her anyhow, always trying to get that extra bit out of me for nothing.'

Mrs Smith then went on to say that she wondered how her former employer had been able to supply such a lavish spread, 'with sandwiches made from thick slices of ham, cut off a big joint of boiled bacon,' adding, 'probably black market.' I felt a pang of envy but also a surge of virtue, as I thought of our pig's wrist menus.

*

I wrote hastily to Cousin Marion today to acknowledge her letter, which was a list of what to expect in a parcel that was already on its way to us. The list was very exciting, when I read it out Clare was so overcome that she had to sit down. We shall watch for the postman in his red van as he nears the cottage. He is very nice and so pleased when something comes that looks interesting. He is also very old and I do not know how he kept going during our last terrible winter. I will send the newspapers for the 14th November to Marion. I am sure there will be much about the Royal Wedding in the Canadian papers but it will be nice for her to read reports and see pictures from the British press.

*

The most dreadful thing happened yesterday. Miss Feather's Nanki-Poo was killed by a bus just outside here. A dealer had called to look at the furniture Miss Feather must dispose of before she goes into the home. When he left he did not shut the front gate. Miss Feather, upset at the miserably low price she had been offered for the furniture, did not check the gate before she let Nanki-Poo out for an airing and he wandered into the road. Her house and ours are on a very dangerous bend in the road; it was a foggy morning and the trolley bus driver did not see such a tiny creature and ran over him. The end was instant. We heard the disturbance but did not realise what had happened.

Miss Feather ran out, saw the situation and fainted. Mr Watson was outside his shop and he picked her up and brought her to us. We revived her with Sal volatile; apart from shock she had suffered little damage, except for a slightly grazed knee. Miss Feather stayed with us the whole day, weeping a great deal. Edith surprised us by being a very devoted comforter, taking Miss Feather up to her own room and putting her to bed. We invited Miss Feather to stay the night but she preferred to go to her own house at dusk, Clare going with her and staying for a while. Mr Watson dealt with the remains, burying the poor creature in the woods, keeping the dog's tiny collar in case Miss Feather wanted a memento. In the cruellest way this sad event has solved the dilemma of Nanki-Poo and the question of who will care for him when Miss Feather moves. Not something one would ever say to his mistress, of course.

*

The death of her dog has had a galvanising effect on Miss Feather. It seems to have made her more accepting of her impending departure from the Ridge and she is laying plans. She has decided that when the Christmas school holidays start, and her maid does not have her work in Hurst Court School, the girl might like to earn extra by helping to pack up "Claremont." We suggested that Clout might be able to spare some time to clear the garden and burn any rubbish. Then Miss Feather astounded us by asking if St Catherine's House could make use of her unwanted furniture, household linen, pictures and books as she had lost heart for the task of selling them. I rang the home's head housekeeper and the offer was gladly accepted. In these straightened times such a gift is very welcome. Miss Feather immediately felt as if a burden had been lifted from her and began to talk of Christmas. We invited her to spend it with us but a friend at her church had planned a round of hospitality to give Miss Feather a good send off.

*

With the shortage of so many things the prospect of buying Christmas gifts is daunting this year. But we had a piece of good fortune. I heard at church about a general store keeper in a nearby village who had inherited the stock of a dress and haberdashery shop, formerly owned by his elderly aunt, who had lived in a small, south east coastal town. At the start of the war, terrified of invasion, she had shut up the shop, complete with its stock and departed hastily to Scotland, to live with her sister. The two ladies had died within days of each other at the end of the war. Her nephew went last week to clear the shop and found a perfect museum. Astonishingly, nothing had been touched! He brought the abandoned goods back to his shop to sell them off. A friend from the Catherine House Committee has access to the occasional use of a car so she and we three went to have a look at his wares. (The shopkeeper said that no clothing coupons were required as the goods were regarded as second hand. I do hope that is correct; I would be deeply ashamed to be a black marketeer).

Confusion greeted us in the shop; bales of cloth and boxes of haberdashery fought for space with sacks of potatoes and boxes of broken biscuits. In a flat above the shop the muddle was worse, even the bath was used to store a bevy of ancient shop dummies; one was perched inelegantly on the lavatory. Clare, who is very fastidious, was all for leaving at once but as soon as Edith spotted the knitting wool and the embroidery silks there was no moving her; so we stayed to explore. Clare unbent a little when I found an unopened box of a dozen pairs of grey, heavy-duty lisle stocking in a size that would fit both her and me, and a bale of beautiful chintz, which would make curtains for the sitting room. The years of bright sunlight has bleached the pattern from our present ones, as we have closed them in the afternoons, to protect the furniture. While Clare was downstairs paying for the purchases I discovered a pair of leather, fur-lined gloves to give to her as a Christmas gift and a pretty scarf for Edith, to add to her collection. They were all pre-war goods, of course, and the better for it.

Edith was desperate for some new drawers but the only ones we could find were gym knickers in dark navy, probably kept in the shop to serve the needs of the several girls' boarding schools near the Sussex Downs, or so said the shopkeeper's wife. Edith disliked the colour but overcame her vanity, accepting that warmth was of paramount consideration, but she asked us to promise not to hang them on the washing line when Clout was working in the garden. A friend who went out to the shop some days later said that almost everything had gone, except for the navy blue gym knickers, which the shopkeeper was displaying in his window marked, "Acceptable Christmas Gift." When Edith got round to wearing hers she said that the itching from the rough fabric was intolerable. I predict we will have a good stock of navy blue "dusters" to start the New Year!

December

Two years ago a man of international notoriety came to live on the Ridge, at the Netherwood Guest House, across the road. We did not know of this at first; the news came to us later via on of the usual sources of gossip, Mrs Smith or Miss Feather; I forget which. The new arrival's name was Aleister Crowley, a purported occultist, or magician as some call him. His name was in the newspapers on and off for years, due to his bizarre beliefs and practices. We came to know him quite well by sight, he was given to taking a daily constitutional along the Ridge and often went about with Mr Watson, from the post office stores; Crowley was never without a smelly pipe gripped in his jaws; Edith was terrified of meeting him, but apart from his eccentric dress and strange comments, he seemed harmless enough; just a sick-looking old man.

He died on 1st December. It was very bleak weather that saw the funeral cortege set off for Brighton Crematorium yesterday morning, if cortege is the correct word for such a small group of mourners. That a man of such infamy should end his life in obscurity could be seen by some as Divine Justice but I do not believe The Divine works in such ways. We had a thunderstorm in the evening; no doubt Mrs Smith will be attaching great significance to that!

Crowley's obituary in The Times said that at 8 years old he had been sent to a strict Evangelical school in St Leonards that was owned by the Habershon Family, an architect of the same name designed a great house on the Ridge and many other buildings. Odd that Crowley should choose to end his days in a town where, as the obituary suggested, he was so miserable. There is so much death now among our contemporaries; a friend of 60 years standing died nearly three weeks ago, after much suffering.

*

Miss Feather called in to see us mid-afternoon. She had come to recount a rigmarole that she had from her maid, who is friendly with a girl employed at nearby St Margaret's Boarding School for Girls. The story went that a pair of St Margaret's pupils was sent on an errand; it was late afternoon and they were told to hurry back before it got dark. As dusk was approaching on their return, they took a short cut by the footpath behind the church. They arrived at the school, breathless from running and fear, in a state of hysteria, saying they had seen the ghost of Aleister Crowley in the middle of a field and he had waved at them. The Headmistress, Miss Batty, could get nothing sensible from the girls. So, fearful of upsetting fee-paying parents for not taking the matter seriously, she called the police. They sent along a fatherly sort of officer, accompanied by a female auxiliary, to speak to the girls. They told him the man was tall, wearing a long black cape and a top hat and carrying a suitcase. They said that the apparition had only waved and did not speak or approach them. The officer, one of the old school and likely experienced in the histrionic tendencies of young ladies, conducted a few discreet investigations. He discovered, as he had possibly suspected, that a family near the school had been holding a children's Christmas tea party, complete with a magician and it was he, taking a short cut home across the fields, the girls had seen. They had heard of Crowley only as an evil magician who had recently died at Netherwood and their imaginations did the rest. The whole episode was a storm in a tea cup or, more appropriately, a top hat. I do hope the girls were not admonished; there may come a time when a truly unpleasant incident occurs and the wrong attitude now could prevent them from seeking help.

*

I have only just got round to sending Christmas greetings to Cousin Marion due to my being stupidly ill again, I hope they get to Canada in time. It has been a very trying year with illness at Lavender Cottage and among our friends, who I have spent much time visiting during the year, when I have been able. Clare and Edith have also been ill and I have done what I could to care for them.

*

Clare and I have been busy making a batch of cakes to see us through the week. I'm afraid many people spend their bread rations on cakes, to which Clare says, most indignantly, 'can't they make their own?' I am surprised that they don't, for the ones from the shop are very inferior. I don't know how people will manage about Christmas puddings but we shall certainly get a home made one. Clare is an excellent manager and turns out some good pastry and biscuits; how she does it on one ounce of fat per head a week I don't know. Food is the main topic in every conversation. We may begin quite a serious talk on the political situation or the latest book but in the end it always comes to what we do or don't eat.

*

I will send a copy of The Strand to Cousin Marion in the absence of any better publication. Things are said to be improving in this respect but I haven't noticed it. In the spring someone lent me a ticket for Boots Library but all the new books are printed in such small type that I cannot read them and if the printing is good the price is sinful. When I was in town last I went into the only real bookshop worth visiting. I happened to see a poetry anthology so, removing my gloves, I picked up the book to see if contained a poem for which I had been searching for some time. Had it done so I would have bought it and sent it to Cousin Marion as a Christmas gift. I was disappointed in my search; as I put the book back I saw a notice "Please do not handle." I can understand such a notice in shop where foodstuffs are on sale but why in a booksellers? Surely the essential joy of choosing and buying a book is in the preliminary browsing. No real book lover will select a book from its outward appearance. This mania for restrictions seems to be spreading into every department of life and it will be a tragedy if it is allowed to invade bookshops.

*

The December editions of magazines and newspapers are printing advertisements to persuade us to buy all manner of things as Christmas gifts, regardless of the fact that many of them are in short supply or far beyond the pockets of most, certainly in Hastings. We are not really poor, but our income is limited, and we have to manage very carefully to allow something for emergencies. The notion of home made Christmas gifts has come to the fore in recent years and ideas and suggestions for such are published, complete with patterns, for all manner of fripperies. Many of which, I feel, will give more pleasure to the maker than the recipient. I have never felt the need for a fancy cape to wear when I apply face powder or a cosy for my egg. I do not use powder and any boiled egg that I may be fortunate enough to have is never obliged to wait before I address it!

*

73

Clare and I have decided to send National Savings Gift Tokens to the younger folk for Christmas this year. It will avoid all that trudging round shops, which none of us are up to at the present time. The tokens come with a nice greetings card. There is so little choice in our shops and the nation is urged to save not spend. It is not only money that is needed for gifts but also, in some cases, clothing coupons. I see from the local paper that at Plummer Roddis two handkerchiefs for men, (the sort I use) are 2/6d and 1 coupon; fleece-lined leather gloves, (not fur-lined, as are those I found for Clare), are 18/10d and two coupons; headscarves 16/6d and one coupon. Fully-fashioned silk stockings are 9/3d and three coupons. Outrageous, but we never wear silk these days. Such a chilly luxury!

*

Householders along this part of the Ridge are in an uproar about tree felling that has been going on between Hastings Cemetery and the Harrow. Clare telephoned Mr Symonds at "Netherwood"; she thought that as a town councillor he would know what was afoot. He didn't but was very concerned; a preservation order that the council had submitted to protect trees along that stretch of the road is waiting the approval of the Minister of Town and Country Planning. I am told that Mr Symonds went out and remonstrated with the tree-fellers, who discontinued their work for the time being. Trees are one of the loveliest of God's creations and for them to be cut down without apparent reason is a wicked act. What would the Ridge be like without its crown of magnificent trees?

*

A party of carol singers toured the Ridge yesterday evening. They sang so tunefully that I think they must have been from a church, probably St Helen's, which, I am informed, has a very well trained choir. Snow would have completed the charming picture as I opened the front door; there was none, but a heavy frost had rimed the bushes and shrubs and everything sparkled in the light from the house. Reluctantly, I had to ask the singers to curtail their performance as Clare was ill in bed and trying to sleep. I hoped that my donation to their collection box softened any abruptness on my part.

*

Two parcels arrived from Canada today and such gorgeous parcels! Out first came two tins of delicious bacon on which we felt inclined to fall tooth and nail at once. Our rations of two thin rashers per fortnight per person have not given us much scope. Later, there arrived a weighty parcel which I carried up to Clare's bedroom; lumbago and a heavy cold are keeping her confined. I'm sure that the parcel had a beneficial effect; she just gloated over it. The dried fruit especially appealed to her housewifely mind, the distribution is very erratic here. The grocer is always very apologetic, 'So sorry. no dates or sultanas this month, we may have some in time for Christmas.' But he didn't.

Cousin Marion's unexpected gift of fruit made us start planning when to make the Christmas pudding. I begged from Clare half the sugar, intending to make some parsnip wine but I felt she thought this rather wasteful. Cousin Marion even included bay leaves and cloves, both a curiosity, as we have not seen them for some time. Edith Lake cast very wistful eyes at the cake sent; we can't keep her off cake if there happens to be one in the offing. I helped her make a pudding yesterday because she has become so forgetful and I am sure she would have left out the suet. The butcher actually sent us some, he is a nice, kind man, even if his meat is leathery, but that is not his fault.

The one person who did not appreciate the parcel was James. I have promised him a bit of salmon one day. He is a spoilt wretch and will not eat meat unless it has onion-flavoured gravy. He really prefers frozen cod, a mercy, as fish is the only un-rationed food. James is well but his temper is variable and if the fish is not fresh he mentions it fluently. He is only a common tabby tom but well-marked and very loving when in a good temper.

*

To my delight a third weighty parcel that arrived contained cheese, I have already nibbled it and look forward to Welsh Rarebit tonight, quite oblivious to indigestion that will surely follow. We don't know how to thank Cousin Marion. Clare says she is trumps and I feel almost sinful at being so fortunate. Edith does not get any nice things sent, except for a salmon that her rich sister bestows on her occasionally, in the summer; but we always share our things with Edith. Clare's brother-in-law is very kind though not rich. Clare's relatives are all very good, though none are wealthy; it is odd that rich people are never as generous as those who are hard up; I suppose it is a fellow feeling. Clare's brother-in-law always brings us baskets of apples and her brother is very good in sending us cigarettes, also her nephew. I do get quite a number given me and I smoke more than I should.

Christmas Pudding

4 ounces self-raising flour
4 ounces margarine
4 ounces breadcrumbs
2 ounces chopped nuts (if available)
4 ounces sugar
4 ounces raisins
4 ounces sultanas

2 ounces currants or prunes
1 level tsp mixed spice
2 tbsp dried egg
rind of orange, if available
pinch of salt
milk to mix

Clean all the dried fruit
Chop nuts finely
Sieve the flour, dried egg and salt into a basin
Add the fruit, nuts, breadcrumbs, sugar, spice and grated orange rind and mil all together.
Melt the margarine, pour over the dried ingredients and stir well
Add a very little milk so that the mixture is moist all through but quite stiff
Cover with greaseproof paper and a pudding cloth and steam for 2 hours
When the pudding is cold remove from pudding cloth and greaseproof paper and cover with clean greaseproof paper and a fresh pudding cloth; this helps the pudding to keep well
Store in a dry place
Before serving, steam again for two hours

Because of the parcel from Canada we are able to add extra dried fruit to the pudding and I put in some parsnip wine, wishing it were brandy. We do not put in the traditional silver sixpences as Edith would be sure to choke on them.

Welsh Rarebit

Cut some bread into slices about 1/2 inch in thickness, toast the bread slightly on both sides without hardening or burning it, Cut some slices of cheese, not quite as large as the bread, put them on the toasted bread and place them under a grill until the cheese is melted; be careful that the cheese does not burn. Spread over the top a little made mustard and a seasoning of pepper, and serve very hot.

*

How vexing to be ill and bed-bound yet again at this busy time of year. I usually help Edith with her cards and letters at Christmas but being in bed and so run down in health has put it beyond me this year. I feel quite owlish. It seems that when I do feel up to helping Edith she cannot or will not co-operate. I suspect she knows that her mind is not as clear as it once was and hence resorts to all sorts of strategies to hide it, by either being 'too busy' or just cross. A few times recently Edith has referred to her mother as if she were still alive, asking if she will be home soon or saying, on hearing a bit of gossip, 'What will mother say to that?' Edith's sister has not visited her for some time and I wonder if we should write to her about this problem. Yet Edith is in excellent physical health and able to attend to her personal needs without any mishaps. We share our living quarters with her at present to save on the heating costs and it gives less work to Edith's maid. This is probably just as well as she under treatment at the hospital and leaves after lunch. She is much older than I realised and cares for an invalid husband. I have only just learned this after all these years. But Edith keeps her so occupied there is never time to chat.

*

The cottage Christmas decorations look very festive this year. We do not have a tree, regarding it as something for children, but we have festooned the pictures frames and shelves with sprays of holly and ivy that Clout gathered for us. Clare took the white distemper brush to the tips of some of the fire-lighter pine cones, to make them appear frosty, lodging them among the greenery. The mantelpiece is crowded with Christmas cards, reminding us of our families and friends. Mrs Smith gave the brass an extra rub just for Christmas. She, like Clout, was pleased with the extra we gave her for Christmas; they do work so hard for us.

*

Dear Clare gave me some smart new carpet slippers for Christmas, saying, 'No wearing them to take peelings up to the compost heap because you can't be bothered to put on shoes.' She was delighted with the gloves I gave her and says she will keep them for best. The scarf for Edith was eclipsed by a very expensive gift. Edith's sister sent her a wireless. It was delivered from a shop in Hastings whilst Edith was resting one afternoon. Her sister telephoned us, saying she would be grateful if we could hide it from Edith until the appointed time. We groaned at the thought of this innovation, as Edith finds it very difficult these days to cope with anything that is in the least bit complicated; we fear we will be for ever running up to her room to adjust the tuning.

*

Who am I to criticise Edith's confusion? I have just found my fountain pen, which I often lose. I am still woolly-headed from the nasty attack of flu. Our butcher was told by the Ministry of Food that there would be no pork for the rations. It did not trouble us as we find pork too indigestible at our age. We did manage to get a fowl for Christmas at a not too exorbitant price; it looked very white and nice, promising a typical Christmas dinner. I got out of my sick-bed to boil it; it's never safe to roast anything these days. I always have the honour of cooking Christmas dinner. Well, I never tasted a worse bird, it was so leathery that our forks refused to penetrate its hide and it ended in soup. Clare said, 'never mind, we've got the ham.' She cooked part of it and it was delicious; it will provide meals for days. The bigger piece sits in the larder and will last no end of time. Clare does all the cooking, though she sometimes lets me take a hand, but not often, as she says we might be fairly well fed on Monday but Friday would find and empty larder! I'm sure that's a slander.

We gave our neighbour Mrs Todd some samples of the butter, lard and cheese from the parcel. She has been so good in helping with home nursing that we are glad to be able help her out with some food. Rationing is particularly hard on single people. We will not eat the Canadian Christmas pudding until a friend, ill at present, can share it with us. Edith cannot wait to be let loose on the cake.

Clare had a telephone call from her brother on Boxing Day to say how sorry they were at being unable make a Christmas-time visit. They were so short of petrol but they hope to come in the New Year. In Kent, where they live, the inhabitants experienced a meteorological drama on Christmas Day. There was one huge, isolated clap of thunder, which, coming so soon after the war, had an un-nerving effect. They had to take in an elderly neighbour, who was near to fainting because she was so terrified. Boxing Day in Hastings gave us wonderful sunshine and clear blue skies after a Christmas Day of high winds and rain. Mr Watson told Clare yesterday that he had heard from the owners of Netherwood Guest House that the hotels in the town were well booked for the holiday, even though some hoteliers feared that the petrol ration would keep visitors away. Somebody saw people strolling along the Hastings seafront or sitting in the promenade shelters on Boxing Day. From what was said in the news one may gather that in spite of austerity most people had had a good time. Mrs Smith told us she crammed all her family into her little house for Christmas dinner, the festive meats being three wild rabbits, which as she said, 'were tastier than chicken.' We would have probably have been better served by rabbit but Edith will not have it in the house.

*

As it turned out our fears about Edith managing her wireless were unjustified; once it was tuned to the BBC Light Programme she would not have it set anywhere else. She particularly enjoys the twice daily "Music While You Work", (not that she does, work, that is,) and she leaves the wireless to strum and chatter all day. Luckily, "Woman's Hour" is transmitted on this wavelength so Edith can indulge in private. In the short time she has had the wireless she seems to have rallied; seeming quite her old self much of the time. One vexing thing is the daily hunt for the Radio Times. We have only one copy, the shortage of newsprint forbids the luxury of two, so during Christmas we were on frequent quests. Edith, who has become uncharacteristically careless, just puts it down where she happens to be, so her new-found interest has its drawbacks.

*

Miss Feather came to say goodbye yesterday. When she had her big clear-out she kept only a dozen books, some of her favourites, three pictures and a few framed photographs, to take to the home. The caretaker from St Catherine's House is going to supervise the removal of the furniture after Miss Feather has departed; as she said she could not bear to see it all go, 'Especially father's desk, where he wrote his sermons.' She invited us to select a picture from those remaining, as a memento; we chose a very pretty watercolour of the Sussex Downs. Miss Feather said she had painted it when she was a girl. While Miss Feather went through a vast collection of letters and documents, Mrs Todd sat with her, giving peaceful moral support. The papers included copies of her father's sermons; a parcel of some of these, along with old family photographs, is to be sent to a nephew, the remainder is to be burned. Mrs Todd said she would take the unwanted papers away and have a bonfire in her garden, to spare Miss Feather's feelings. She is leaving before New Year's Eve, as she said, 'to start a new year in a new home.' I am sure that she will settle well and that her kind nature will gain her friendships. We promised to write to her, another for my list, and give her the latest gossip. But where we will hear it when Miss Feather has gone I do not know.

*

We did not sit up to see the New Year in. Edith retired early to listen to her radio and fell asleep while it strummed away. The chimes of Big Ben awoke Clare and me so we went down to toast the arrival of 1948 in cocoa. We talked about Miss Feather's situation, which has stirred fresh concern for us about our occupancy of the cottage. We must make a determined effort in the New Year to get Edith to the solicitor to add a codicil to her will about our future security. A smaller problem is what to do with this diary. Clare has never read it and I am hard put to it to decide whether she would find it amusing or irritating.

*

To discover how life continued for the three ladies at Lavender Cottage and more background to their lives and that of their neighbours, read the companion books to this: "Letters from Lavender Cottage" and "The Long Road to Lavender Cottage", both by Victoria Seymour

Background to Emilie Crane's Play

"Boy Wanted" was previously published in the second of the Lavender Cottage series; Emilie's diary has put her play into context, warranting a reprise.

*

It was natural that Emilie should select a vehicle for the publication of her play that matched her principles: The Boy's Own Paper was middle-class, nonconformist and had a close association with the kind of pupils to whom Emilie's career was dedicated. The BOP was characterized by a tone of Christian morality and had originally included boys of all social backgrounds. Eventually, poorer readers were sidelined and the content of the paper was aimed at public and grammar school boys.

The BOP published the work of nonentities like Emilie and also famous authors and sportsmen. It had a keen readership throughout the 1920s and into the 1930s. But after 1939, no doubt due in part to the effects of war, the paper went into decline and never really recovered, publishing its last edition in 1967.

The play's subtitle, "A Breaking-up Piece", indicates it was an entertainment to be performed by the pupils at the end of a school term, then a traditional part of school life. The performance is set in a city office and it depicts the comical struggles of the boss to find a suitable office boy. Emilie's eccentric sense of fun permeates the plot. The date of the edition of the Boy's Own Paper, in which Emilie's play appeared, was February 1921, the month of her 50th birthday.

*

BOY WANTED

A Breaking-up Piece

by Emilie Crane.

CHARACTERS.

MR GUMBLENAG. (A business man).
THE LIVELY BOY.
THE SLOW BOY
THE DEMON KING
THE PERFECTLY PERFECT BOY
MR ABRAHAM NOAH (a client of MR GRUMBLENAG)
AUNT MARIA (MR GRUMBLENAG'S maiden aunt)

Scene: A city office. To the left, a table with papers, circulars, envelopes, inkstand, box for stamps and a bell.

Left Centre, MR GRUMBLENAG'S coat and hat hanging on a peg. Right centre, an imitation telephone; chairs, long broom in corner; duster and stove brush in convenient place.

MR GRUMBLENAG discovered sitting at a table reading a letter. He places it in an envelope, directs it, and looks round, then takes out his watch.

MR. G. Ten o'clock and not a boy turned up yet. How on earth am I going to get anything done without a soul to run an errand or mind the office? (In a grumbling tone) Not that boys are any good when one does get them! Always got the face-ache when there's work to be done; making themselves ill gorging sweet stuff all day long and want to go and bury their grandmothers every time there's a football match on! I don't know what boys are coming to! When I was a boy – (knock heard) Ah, There's someone-perhaps it's a boy after the situation. (another knock.) Come in! (Enter the LIVELY BOY, rather dirty, very untidy but sharp-looking.)

MR G. Well, who are you?

L. B. (with strong Irish accent) Plaze sorr, I'm a bhoy.

MR G. I can see that you aren't a girl. What do you want?

L. B. Plaze sorr, I've come after the place.

MR G. Come after the place, have you? Have your brought your references?

L. B. Plaze sorr, me mother says me rifernces is in me face.

MR G. Well, my lad, perhaps if you'd washed your face a bit more, I might have been able to see them. Anyway, what can you do?

L. B. Me mother says I kin do anything sorr.

MR G. Oh, no doubt your mother thinks you're an angel! Most mothers do.

L. B. No sorr, plaze sorr, -she calls me a little varmint mostly.

MR G. All boys are that but I don't suppose you are any worse than the rest of them. I don't as a rule take a boy with out a character, but as you look pretty bright I am willing to give you a trial.

L.B. Thank ye, sorr.

MR. G. You had better begin right away: there's plenty to do. Suppose you take that duster and give the place a good dust up. It hasn't been done since my last boy went.
(MR. G. goes on with his work while the LIVELY BOY takes duster and begins dusting with the utmost rapidity; he dashes at the chairs and dusts them, falling over in the process; he dusts the telephone, the walls, the floor and MR G.'s overcoat and then starts on MR. G.'s top hat, taking it off the peg and rubbing it vigorously-MR G looks up)

MR.G. (angrily). What are you doing, you clumsy young idiot? Don't you know how to treat a gentleman's hat? Don't touch it with that dirty rag. Give it a good brush if you want to. That won't hurt it. (goes on reading).

L. B. Yis, sorr. (looks round, sees the stove brush, picks it up and begins brushing the hat with it, pretending to spit on it as he brushes. The hat begins to assume the appearance of the 'fretful porcupine'. MR.G. looks up again).

MR G. (jumping up angrily and snatching the hat away).You silly nincompoop! What are you doing? You've ruined the hat! Goodness gracious, isn't it possible to get hold of a boy with a grain of sense in him? My only decent hat! (smoothing it as he speaks) And Aunt Maria will be here soon and I'll have to take her out to lunch! Oh, you idiot! (Telephone rings) There, go and answer the telephone.

L.B. Yis, sorr. (goes to the telephone, looks at it, scratches his head, shakes it and looks at MR G.; the telephone bell ringing all the while).

MR G. What, don't you know how to answer the telephone yet? Take the receiver off the hook and put it to your ear. The receiver donkey' that thing there! Comes to the telephone and lifts the receiver.) Hold it to your ear like that and put your mouth to the speaking- tube. (gives the boy the receiver). Now, answer the person politely.

L.B. Yis sorr. (speaking through the tube) Halloo yerself! (listens, and turns round) Plaze sorr, it's a female lidy and she says, "Are ye there dear?"

MR G. (who has take up his papers again) Well, well, answer her.

L.B.(shouts into the tube). Yis, me old darlin', meself's here!

MR G. (jumping up). What's that? What are you saying? Here, come away from there. (pushes boy aside and takes the receiver). No, no, my dear- nothing of the sort-I assure you - it's that new boy of mine-now do listen to me! You're quite wrong my dear-it's all a mistake-no one ever dreamed of such a thing-oh well- if you won't listen-(hangs up receiver with a despairing look and turns to the boy) Now you've done it, you precious piece of brightness! That's my wife and she's in a pretty tantrum. Says I've put someone up to insult her and has gone into hysterics. Won't there be row when I get home? As if I hadn't enough to worry me without this. Well, you've done enough mischief for one day. The sooner you get out of this the better it will be for you. Look sharp and get out! Go home and tell your mother to try and knock a little sense into you with a good-sized broom handle! D' ye hear?

L.B. Yis, sorr. (Exit).

MR. G. (pacing the room) There goes another of them! They're all alike, not a pin to choose between them for ignorance and stupidity. Now what am I to do? Here's the morning nearly gone and not a stroke of work done. All these circulars to get off today and not a letter answered! (clutches his hair) And Noah will be along in a minute or two after the money I owe him and how am I to put him in a good temper with my nerves like fiddle-strings? It's enough to drive a man mad!

(throws himself into his chair, and leans his head on his hand. A heavy dragging sound is heard outside and then the noise of someone falling against the door. Enter the SLOW BOY, dragging his feet along the floor. He is a lumpish-looking youth, with a vacant look in his eyes and his mouth open in a wide grin. He comes up to the table).

MR.G. (looking up.) Well, what do you want?

S. B. (in a hoarse voice). A've come arter the job.

MR G. Well, why don't you take your hat off when you are speaking to a gentleman?

(The S.B. removes his hat slowly with both hands and puts it down on MR G's. paper's.)

MR G. Not there stupid! Hang it up.

(The S.B. goes to the wall and tries to hang his hat on a peg; it falls off. After several attempts, during which he looks round at the audience and grins, he manages to persuade the hat to stay on the peg).

S.B.(to the world in general.)That's my best 'at, that is, and mother told me to be very careful with that there 'at. (He comes back to the table, brings a large apple out of his pocket and takes a huge bite out of it).

MR G. What are you doing? Haven't you had any breakfast this morning?

S.B. Yus, but me mother says a'm a growin' lad and wants feedin' up.

MR. G. Oh, well, you can't be fed up here, unless it's with work! Put that away at once.

(S.B. stuffs the apple in his pocket reluctantly, wipes his mouth with the back of his hand and grins at MR.G.)

MR. G. (aside). What a boy, he's a perfect fool! (Aloud) So you've come after the situation; do you know anything about the duties of an office boy?

S. B. Naw!

MR. G. Say, "No, sir."

S. B. "Naw, sir."

MR. G. Well, that's honest at any rate. Have you brought your references? (The S. B. stares vacantly at MR. G., scratches his head, then pulls out the contents of his pockets and lays them on the table; the gnawed apple, some string, a piece of bread and butter, pocket knife, etc, etc.)

S. B. Them's all I brought with me.

MR.G. Great Scott! Are you an idiot boy? Don't you know what references are? (The S. B. shakes his head slowly)

S. B. Are they them things as goes to football matches?

MR G. (impatiently) Football matches! There, it's no use talking to you. I can quite see you won't be an ounce of good but if you like to stay for the day and make yourself useful we'll see how you get on. I've got to have a boy of some sort, and you may turn out better than you look. Here (holding out a letter he has written) I want this to go to the post at once. You'll find a stamp in that box. (The S. B. takes the letter, looks at it, goes to the box, picks out a stamp and brings it and the letter back to MR. G.)

MR. G. (irritably) I don't want it, stupid. Stock on yourself!

(The S. B. looks at MR. G., looks at the letter, looks at the stamp, looks at MR G. again and ends by sticking the stamp on his own cheek.)

MR. G. (jumping up). What are you doing? Give me the letter, booby. (snatches letter). Oh, you'll drive me mad. Here, sit down and see if you can't do something properly. Fold these circulars and put them in these envelopes; they must be got off today. I suppose you can do a simple thing like that without making a fool of yourself?

(MR. G. resumes his work. The S. B. picks up half-a-dozen circulars at once, crushes them together and tries to squeeze them into an envelope. The envelope splits; he throws it on the floor and takes another, with the same result. After doing this several times he manages to get the circulars in, licks the flap and thumps it on the table with a mighty bang. MR. G. looks up)

Mr. G. Whatever are you up to? (picks up the envelope and tears it open) Why, you everlasting noodle, you've sent six circulars to one man? Don't you know better than that? And look at the mess you've made of them! Do you call that folding? Haven't you got any common-sense at all? (looks down and sees the floor strewn with torn envelopes) Oh, that's the limit! Get out of my office you great hulking lout; you're ten thousand times worse than the other one! Take your hat and clear out! D'ye hear me? Don't stand gaping at me! Get out!
(The S. B. goes slowly to the peg, takes his hat, smooths it and puts it on his head then edges towards the door, grinning all the time.) Get a move on and don't grin at me or I'll give you something to make you grin in a different fashion! (The S.B. goes out, still grinning)

MR. G. (throwing himself in a chair and wiping his forehead). Did anyone ever come across such a hopeless noodle? Is it possible that in the whole wide world there isn't a singe boy with a particle of common-sense in him? Talk of the march of progress! Why on earth doesn't someone invent an automatic boy who will do as he is told and only what he is told; who won't stuff himself all day long with toffee and green apples; won't bury his grandmother twice a week in the football season, and above all who can't say more than, "Yes, sir" and "No, sir"! Oh, I'm sick of the whole race of boys. I feel as tired as a dog after what I have gone through this morning. (Yawns and stretches himself) Suppose I must set to and do the work myself-confound these boys! (Getting sleepier.) Aunt Maria and Noah will be in soon. (his head nods and he drops off into a doze, muttering) Confound all boys- rascally lot-all idiots!

THE DREAM.

(The lights go down. A bang is heard off. Enter the DEMON KING with the PERFECTLY PERFECT BOY, who walks rigidly and automatically. Mr. G. looks up but it must be understood that he is supposed to be asleep and dreaming.)

D. K. (presenting the boy to Mr. G.)

This is the Perfectly Perfect Boy:

He can't do anything to annoy;

He can't eat apples, or sweets or cake,

Because his inside's of clockwork make

He's always neat and he's always clean;

He's seldom heard though he may be seen;

He can't be cheeky, because, you know

He can't say more than "yes" or "no";

If you wind him up in the morning-so (winding Boy.)

The whole day long he'll keep on the go;

If you treat him with care, you'll find him a joy.

(aside) I wonder!

Because he's a perfectly perfect boy!

(Exit the D. K. accompanied by another bang).

Mr. G. (staring at the P.P. Boy) Well. I didn't quite catch all the gentleman said but I understand you are a perfectly perfect boy?

P.P.B. (in a squeaky voice) Yes, sir.

Mr G. And are you sure you know your work?

P. P. B. No, sir.

Mr. G. Eh! What do you mean?

P.P.B. Yes.sir.

Mr. G. That's better. Well you can't be worse than the other specimens I've had here and there's one thing about you-you do look clean. Almost too clean for a boy. How many times a day do you wash your face-a dozen times?

P.P.B. No, sir.

Mr. G. Half-a dozen?

P.P. B. Yes, sir.

Mr. G. Good gracious, what a boy! Washes his face six times a day! I begin to think I've found a treasure at last. Now my lad let's see what you can do. For a start, suppose you take a broom and clear up all this litter on the floor.

(Mr. G. turns to his papers and the P.P. B. walks stiffly to the broom, hold it rigidly and begins sweeping the floor. Presently the broom collides with Mr. G's chair and after the fashion of clockwork toys when they meet an obstacle, the P.P.B. keeps jerking it against the chair. Mr. G. looks round)

Mr. G. Oh you want me to move, do you?
(moves himself and the chair to the side of the table. P.P.B. follows him up with broom; business repeated until Mr, G. gets fidgety.)
Mr. G. There, that will do! (aside) Goes a bit to extremes this boy but ant any rate he seems thorough.

(P.P.B. replaces broom)

Mr. G. (aloud) You might run round to the post office with this letter and bring back some more stamps while you are about it-I shall want them. No, stop, on second thoughts I'll go myself- a breath of air will do me good. You can be putting these circulars in while I'm out. (puts on his hat and coat) Before I go, just listen, and be sure not to forget what I am going to say.

P.P.B. No sir.

Mr. G. I'm expecting a gentleman to call this morning, a Mr. Abraham Noah. You'll know him by his clothes; he always wears a rather gaudy tie and a big tie-pin. Also he has a decided nose. I don't particularly want to see him and you may tell him you don't know when I'll be back –say it's uncertain and then perhaps he won't wait. If you can manage to get him out of the office before I return, I shall be uncommonly glad.

P.P.B. Yes, sir.

Mr. G. I don't mind telling you, as you seem a sensible sort of boy, that I owe him some money, and it isn't quite convenient to pay him just now.

P.P.B. No Sir.
Mr. G. (aside) A very intelligent boy this! (aloud) Now if a lady should call- I'm expecting one- a rather elderly lady dressed in a peculiar style, you must be very careful what you say to her.
P. P. B. Yes, sir.

Mr. G. You see, that lady's my aunt and I specially want to see her. So mind you make her take a chair and keep her till I come back – whatever you do, don't let her go.

P.P. B. No, Sir.

Mr. G. I see you quite understand (aside). Really, a most sensible boy! (aloud) Well, now I'm off.

(takes up his stick and exits. The P.P.B. sits at the table and begins folding the circulars, in a jerky fashion. Enter Mr. Abraham, a flashily dressed gentleman, with a large nose).

Mr. N. Well, my young buck, guv' nor in?

P.P.B. Yes, sir.

Mr. N. Well, tell him Mr. Noah's here and wishes to speak to him.

P.P.B. No, sir.

Mr. N. No, not "No" Noah; N-O-A-H-Noah, do you understand?

P.P.B. Yes, sir.

Mr. N. Well, be off and find him. I can't hang about all day waiting for him. Get a move on you! (boy walks off) What a rum walk that chap has! Looks as if he's worked by a propeller!

(Mr. N. wanders round the room, looks at papers on the table, picks up a circular and reads it; gets impatient, looks at his watch and goes to door)

Mr. N. Come on, young fellow; are you going to be all day?

(the P.P. B. returns)

Mr. N. Well, is he coming?

P. P. B. No, sir.

Mr. N. What d'ye mean? Did you give him my message?

P.P.B. Yes, sir.

Mr. N. And what did he say?

P.P. B. No, sir.

Mr. N. "No, sir," indeed! What sort of an answer is that? Like his impudence! I'll " no, sir " him! Does he think I'm going to advance him my hard-earned money and only charge him ninety-nine per cent interest to be put off with an answer like that! What does he take me for? Does he think I'm a fool?

P.P.B. Yes, sir,

Mr. N. I'll "yes sir" you, you impertinent young sauce-box. Take that! (boxes P.P B's ear. Boy's arm jerks out automatically and knocks Mr. N. down)

Mr. N. (getting up and furious) You young scoundrel, how dare you? (rushes at boy who again knocks him down. After more business of this sort, Mr. N. is driven towards the door, shaking his fist and shouting.) I'll have the law on you for this and on your master too. He's put you up to this. But I'll teach the pair of you a lesson. I'll have my money out of him in double quick time. Tell him he needn't expect any mercy from me. I'll show him. (As he backs out, shaking his fist at the Boy he nearly knocks over an elderly lady, dressed in mid-Victorian style, who is just entering.) My Dear Madam, a thousand pardons! I did not see you! I trust I have not hurt you?

Aunt Maria. (a little flustered but dropping a genteel curtsey.) No sir, thank you, not at all.

Mr. N. (raising his hat). It's very good of you to say so, Madam; I can assure you it was quite unintentional, my knocking into you like that.

A. M. Please don't mention it sir. (another curtsey).

Mr N. Good morning, madam.

A.M. Good morning, sir.

(Mr. N. goes off with final shake of his fist at the boy).

A.M. (taking a large fan from a reticule, which she carries, and fanning herself) Boy, is my nephew, Mr. Grumblenag in?

P.P.B. No, sir.

A.M. (indignantly) What do you mean by calling me sir, you jackanapes? "Sir" indeed! Don't you know how to talk to a lady? Do I look like a man?

P.P.B. Yes, sir.

A.M. How dare you? A man indeed! And I, a respectable maiden lady that has hardly looked at a man in her life! To be likened to a nasty, dirty, smoky man! Men! Why, I wouldn't touch the best of them with a red hot poker! Thank goodness I never had anything to do with men.(coyly) Not but what they were much attracted to me in my younger days and even now I fancy I have my share of good looks! (sharply) What are you grinning at boy? Don't you believe me?

P.P.B. No, sir.

A.M. Oh, this boy will drive me mad! What does my nephew mean by having such a boy about the place? Does he keep you here to insult visitors?

P.P.B. Yes, sir.

A.M. This is perfectly outrageous! I won't stay here a minute longer. You tell my nephew when he comes in, young man, that I shall expect a full explanation of your conduct, and an ample apology from him before I set foot in his office again. I was never so treated in my life.
(She is going off when the P.P.B. gets in front of her and holds out his arms stiffly to prevent her exit).

A. M. What are you doing? Let me pass at once! Oh, the boy's stark, staring mad!

(P.P.B. and A. M. dodge about, until finally the Boy drives the old lady into a chair, where he holds her down; she shrieks and utters protests but finally collapses into a state of terrified quietness.   Enter Mr. G in a state of agitation; he does not see the others at first.)

Mr. G. I can't think what has happened to upset Noah. Wonder why he wouldn't stop and speak to me just now-just shook his fist in my face and went off muttering about having the law on me! Evidently he'd just come from here-I hope that boy of mine didn't say anything to upset him-it would be frightfully awkward if he insists on having his money just now-
(A.M gives a terrified gasp Mr. G. looks round.)

Mr. G. Aunt Maria! What are you doing to the lady you young idiot? Let her go at once (pulls Boy away)

A.M. (getting up in a tremendous rage). Don't talk to me! Don't talk to me! I have never been so insulted in my life. You did this on purpose Charles Grumblenag; you set that boy on to insult me, I know you did! This is one of your silly jokes, is it? You won't find it much of a joke though! I'll be even with you! I'll make you suffer for it! I'll cut you off with a shilling, yes I will! I'll leave all my money to the Society for the Propagation of Pug Dogs! Not a penny do you get and don't you think it!
(pushes Mr. G. aside and goes off muttering) Not a single penny – never was so insulted!

Mr. G. (clasping his head despairingly) Good Heavens! What has happened to me? What a horrible state of things! Noah frantic with rage for some reason or other and Aunt Maria gone to cut me off with a shilling! I must be having a bad dream. (to P.P.B.) And you're the cause of it, you bag of unutterable idiocy! I suppose it was you who upset Noah when he called? Didn't you behave civilly to him?

P.P.B. No, sir.

Mr. G. I thought as much! Well, it will please you to know that you've ruined me. I'm done for if he calls his money in. I shan't be able to borrow any from Aunt Maria, that's certain! And she won't leave me a penny in her will, either! Here's a pretty state of things! This is what comes of taking on a Perfectly Perfect Boy! Why wasn't I satisfied with the ordinary sort of boy, who just did the ordinary sort of damage- spoilt my things and got on my nerves and tried my temper! He wouldn't have let me in for this at any rate. I've half a mind to break your head for you! (makes a move towards the Boy, who shoots out his arm and knocks Mr. G. into his chair. Mr. G. stares at him helplessly. The stage grows dark. Bang heard off. Enter the DEMON KING).

D. K.

My automatic boy, I find,

Has failed to meet approval;

And so it just remains to me

To hasten his removal.

But ere we go, a parting word

To you who seek perfection:

It won't be found in any boy

Of whom you make selection.

"Boys will be boys" – remember that,

Have patience with their blunders;

With all their faults, they're better than

Your automatic wonders.

And for the rest, take comfort, for

Things aren't just what they seem:

Awake and find what's past to be

No other than a dream!

(Exeunt D. K. and P. P. B. Lights)

Mr. G. (waking and looking about him in a dazed fashion.)

A dream! Only a dream! Then it hasn't all happened. There never was Perfectly Perfect Boy! Noah didn't shake his fist in my face and say he'd have the law on me! And Aunt Maria hasn't been and she hasn't cut me off with a shilling and left all her money to the Society for the Propagation of Pug Dogs. Thank goodness! Only a dream! But what nightmare! Phew! No more Perfectly Perfect Boys for me! He's taught me a lesson, anyhow and one I shan't forget in a hurry. Automatic obedience by itself is about as useful as an addled egg and can do a lot more harm. In future I'll stick to the ordinary common or garden boy and make the best of him and his blunders. Now, let's get to work. (takes up his papers.)

Curtian

Supplies Are Limited

The following collection of advertisements, taken from 1947 editions of a popular magazine, reliably documents the conditions of the period.

Companies, keen to regain the loyalty of pre-war customers, published adverting material that was, in some cases, merely a promise of things to come in better times. The adverts were printed in monochrome and to limited sizes, reflecting the post-war restriction on newsprint and the rarity of colour printing.

Readers may be repelled by the casual racism in the drinking chocolate advertisement or the extolling of the potential of an underarm deodorant to protect for seven days. But this is how it was in 1947.

100

" - so some **BRYLCREEM** is still obtainable "

Yes, but like most good things it's scarce. Perhaps it won't be so long now before more plentiful times come round. Meanwhile when you do get a bottle use it sparingly.

This famous Milk is now partially released for domestic use. More ample supplies will become available as conditions improve.

THERE'S INTERNATIONAL AGREEMENT ON

Coca-Cola

TRADE MARK REG.

Everywhere people approve the pure refreshing goodness of COCA-COLA — for who could resist that cheerful sparkle and that uncommonly delicious flavour? When you are able again to choose your soft drink by *name*, you will be able once more to buy and enjoy COCA-COLA and rely on its unvarying excellence.

DELICIOUS AND REFRESHING

The registered trade marks "Coca-Cola" and "Coke" distinguish the product of The Coca-Cola Co. Ltd.

THE CHRISTMAS SEARCH
FOR EVERSHARP
IS HERE

*Leave time to find
something with a
non-austerity feel —an
Eversharp. Not many about
—but though the quantity is
small, there are many models.
Try your stationer or jeweller for :
The new Eversharp 4-square pencil, in
black or pastel shades at 6/- ; the
silver-plated Eversharp at 8/8d or 11/4d; the
solid silver Eversharp at 27/6d or 36/8d; the
Kingswood pens by Eversharp cost 14/- or 20/-
And for a very special person the gold-filled Eversharp
at 36/8d to 45/10d. (Prices include New Purchase Tax)*

E V E R S H A R P

Eversharp Products are made in Great Britain, Canada and the U.S.A.

"*Shall we sample their* SILLABUBS AND FLUMMERIES?"

In 1817 a new luxury came to London. In Mayfair a shop was opened for the sale of iced delicacies : sillabubs and flummeries (iced fruit with cream and wine) became the fashionable, but expensive, vogue. To-day, ices and iced drinks are within the reach of all. And soon— perhaps in 1947—the blessings of refrigeration *in the home* will be available, too. The new Prestcolds are on the way! And that means : milk that never 'turns '— food kept fresh and appetising — exciting sweets — your own ices. Plan now for a Prestcold, better-than-ever due to wartime experience and progress !

PRESTCOLD Refrigeration

A PRODUCT OF THE PRESSED STEEL CO., LTD.
COWLEY, OXFORD

"*Prestcold will make Refrigeration an every household word*"

Thanks for the applause!

We knew listeners would like our 5-valve all-wave superhet receiver, and we were right ! Although supplies are limited this set is well worth a little patience . . . a first-rate all-rounder, with particularly fine quality and good short wave sensitivity. Ask your radio dealer.

G.E.C.

MANUFACTURERS OF
RADIO & TELEVISION

Prices of the radio receiver illustrated above :

AC MODEL   **£15.15** *(plus £3.7.9 purchase tax)*
AC/DC MODEL   **£16.16** *(plus £3.12.3 purchase tax)*

A SEAT BY THE FIRE

In a few moments, two people will come back into the room, close the door and settle down to enjoy the precious last half hour before going to bed.

"Who are they?" you ask.

Two people whose energy has been sapped by the work and worry of the day . . . people who need the promise of deep sleep tonight and fresh vigour tomorrow . . . a promise most surely contained in those two glasses of Horlicks standing ready on the table.

Horlicks is still not plentiful, but the shops are sharing out what they have as fairly as possible.

HORLICKS

JEYES' FLUID

IN THE HOME

Wet or fine, household chores must be done. Let Jeyes' Fluid help you. It is both a household disinfectant and a cleanser, and will quickly remove dirt from floors, lino, paint, etc. A tablespoonful in every gallon of cleaning water makes work easier — and you disinfect as you clean.

The Guaranteed Germicide

IN THE GARDEN

Good clean soil is the secret of fine crops. Now is the time to sterilise the soil. Use a tablespoonful of Jeyes' Fluid in a gallon of water to each square yard when digging. In clean soil, seeds and seedlings develop more quickly and can better withstand climate changes and attack by garden pests.

JEYES' SANITARY COMPOUNDS COMPANY LIMITED, LONDON, E.13

110

For first class **stew**

Marmite is the making of all stews, gravies, soups, meat and vegetable dishes. It adds delicious flavour and makes the most of rationed food.

Being a Yeast Extract, Marmite provides Vitamins of the B_2 group, of which yeast is a natural source.

always use

MARMITE

In Jars : 1 *oz.* **8d.**, 2 *oz.* **1/1**, 4 *oz.* **2/-**, 8 *oz.* **3/3**, 16 *oz.* **5/9** *from all Grocers and Chemists.*

but I've got a tin of NESCAFÉ

Sheer delight—when at last you find a tin of Nescafé and enjoy rich, full flavoured coffee made right in the cup —no grounds, no bother. And the last spoonful is as deliciously fragrant as the first, for the flavour and aroma are *sealed in* by the special Nestlé process.

(28)

A NESTLÉ'S PRODUCT

NEW WORLD WATER HEATER

FOR GAS APPLIANCES say

NEW WORLD
—it makes a world of difference

Single-point storage type Water Heater gives automatic, instantaneous and plentiful supply of hot water for domestic use. Heat automatically controlled by the Regulo.

12

PRODUCT OF Radiation Ltd

but... will she be as sweet at the END of the day?

Day-long freshness is an art. Pause *before* you dress — for a quick application of Odo-ro-no. Thus you stop perspiration before it starts. Your underarm remains sweet and dry, odour-free. Odo-ro-no saves your clothes *and* your charm.

LIQUID

ODO-RO-NO

FOR COMPLETE
UNDERARM PROTECTION

Odo-ro-no Liquid in two strengths. REGULAR (lasts for 7 days). INSTANT (3 days). Medium and small sizes.

"PACKETS?"

"THOSE ARE THE
THINGS THAT ARE SHORT"

Many articles can only be sold in containers which are made from waste paper—the paper you may thoughtlessly be burning or throwing away. Please save every scrap of waste paper — it is valuable raw material. For instance, one ton of waste paper makes 15,680 cleansing powder canisters.

★ *Shortage of labour has sometimes made the collection of waste paper difficult, but this problem is now becoming easier —so please save all your waste paper for the collector.*

Crystal Gazer Rewarded!

The special qualities of Phoenix materials and the skilled craft of fashioning them were early regarded as essential to the war effort. Phoenix glass met stern tests in the crucible of war, and with developments in research will emerge still fitter to fashion the beautiful clear glass oven-ware so greatly prized by housewives. Here is one young housewife fortunate enough to secure a Phoenix clear glass oven dish. Supplies are still limited, but it is hoped that they will soon increase.

PHOENIX

THE CLEAR GLASS OVEN-WARE

Clear and Stays Clear

GREET NEWS!
always in quality street
now in EVERY street

Mackintosh's
'Quality Street'
ASSORTMENT ~

John Mackintosh & Sons, Ltd., Toffee Town, Halifax.

119

ROWNTREE'S COCOA
So grateful — so genial — so GOOD

Sharps
THE WORD FOR
TOFFEE

EDWARD SHARP & SONS LTD.
of Maidstone, Kent
"THE TOFFEE SPECIALISTS"

Is your dog a danger to other road users?

Train your Dog in road sense — then he'll *live* to see the day when there are plenty of —

SPRATT'S

Restricted supplies at present of . . .

"BONIO"—*the Bone-shaped Biscuit*
"OVALS"—*Pocket Dog Biscuits*
"WEETMEET"—*Granulated Biscuit*

SPRATT'S PATENT LTD.

SHE WILL

EXPECT

THE BEST!

GIVE
HER A *Vactric*
THE FINEST MAID

It may be her knees or her nylons, but you won't catch her bending!

For su:h low level labour as brushing carpets, she's been used to the finest vacuum cleaner that money can buy, so she will expect a VACTRIC!

VACTRIC LTD.. 149 REGENT ST.. LONDON. W.I.

Model R.45
£12-12-0
Tax
£4-14-6
Extra

This is part of a Weston's Cream Cracker

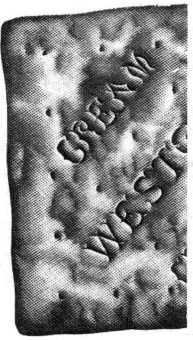

but you cannot visualise the smooth flavour, the flaky lightness and the seductive crackle. You must try them to know what exceptional cream crackers these really are. Supplies are sent everywhere, though at present in limited quantities —but when you have once tasted them you will ask for Weston's Cream Crackers ever after. 1/2d. a pound.

Weston's BISCUITS

Great Scotch !

Old Angus is a noble Scotch, a great Scotch, but how rare it is these days. Even now that strictly limited whisky distillation is being permitted again, we must go gently with our stocks until the new whisky has had its years of maturing. In this way, we shall ensure that now and always, old friends may meet and talk with old friends, warmed by the amber glow of Old Angus.

A NOBLE SCOTCH
—Gentle as a lamb

OLD ANGUS

THE WHITE-WAY
TO BEAT
THE BLACK MARKET

Our British Wines are still sold at a very economical price and represent the best value in wine obtainable today. They are of full alcoholic strength and the name "WHITEWAY" on a label has been a guarantee of purity and quality for over 50 years.

Supplies are limited but moderate quantities are available from wine merchants and licensed grocers

WHITEWAY'S
BRITISH WINES

CVS-96

Food Ration Allocations in Great Britain 1947

Per Person a Week

1 ounce of bacon

2 ounces of butter

3 ounces of margarine

1 ounce cooking fat

2 ounces of cheese

8 ounces of sugar

2 ounces of tea

4 ounces of sweets

4 ounces of jam or marmalade

1 shilling and tuppence worth of meat. (6p)

The price limit on meat was a fair way of rationing as it made more generous quantities of the cheaper cuts of meat available to big families. Offal, i.e.: liver kidney, heart etc, were not rationed, but not easy to buy, as they were often saved for regular or favoured customers.

3 pounds of potatoes per person per week

2 ½ pints of milk per person per week

8 ounces of bread per day

1 egg, when available, per ration book

Points-rationed food –four points could be surrendered per week.

Some of the foods on points were tinned foods, biscuits, jams, jellies and syrup. The points system came to an end in May 1949.

Wartime Rationing in Canada

After WWII began, some imported foods were strictly limited in Canada, as the merchant ships that had formerly carried these goods were deployed for war service. To make matters worse, many merchant ships were destroyed by enemy submarines.

Sugar, coffee, tea, butter, meat and a number of other food items were in short supply. (Sugar was required for the manufacture of shells and bombs, bringing about a further shortage).

Food was also being sent by Canada to Europe, to keep both soldiers and civilians in good health.

Munitions and other forms of war production required tin, thus reducing supplies to canning factories.

In January 1942, a food rationing system began in Canada.

Initially, each person was allowed to buy 12 ounces of sugar a week and a limited amount of coffee and tea, the sugar allotment was later reduced to 8 ounces per week.

In December 1942, butter was added to the ration list, with each person being allowed half a pound per person per week. The government set the prices for the rationed goods.

Petrol was rationed in April 1942.

Rationing of meat began in May 1943, allowing two pounds per week per person.

Additional basic foods came under the strict rules in December 1943: Apple and honey butters, maple syrup, tinned evaporated milk and molasses were all stringently controlled. (Molasses was used in the manufacture of synthetic rubber.) In 1944, cheese, tinned blueberries and pie fillings were also rationed. As the war-time measures progressed, beer was added to the rationed items; alcohol was scarce and highly-priced.

The use of ration books continued in Canada until some time after the war ended; Europe's farmlands and factories were in ruins and foodstuffs, especially meat, continued to be sent from Canada as emergency aid.

Household Hints

It's likely that many of these pre-war, wartime and austerity household hints were known to and used by Emilie Crane and her Lavender Cottage friends. They are included here as a matter of historic interest only. The author gives no guarantee as to their effectiveness and urges caution in their use; particularly in the case of the recipe for "old-fashioned cough cordial."

Uses for Wood Ash
The clean white ash, collected after a wood fire, should be kept in a jar near the scullery sink, as it is valuable for removing stains on metal and china, and makes a good scouring mixture.

Home Made Wood Filler
A cheap home made filler can be made by soaking waste paper in water until it forms a pulp, then adding glue or paste to the mixture. This can be pressed into holes and cracks, spread over with the back of a knife, and allowed to dry thoroughly. When the repair is hard and dry, rub the surface smooth with fine glass-paper. Any particularly large holes should be filled with wood fillets. The pulp is useful only for small repairs. Putty or plaster of Paris can be used for any small irregularities of the surface.

Uses for Vinegar

A few drops of vinegar in a tumbler of water makes an excellent mouth wash.

If you have a bad headache, a handkerchief dipped in vinegar and placed on the forehead often cures the pain.

Vinegar in washing up water removes grease, brightens your china and disinfects.

Salt and vinegar mixed together will take away stains on your china and also cleans the interior of flower vases, water bottles and tumblers.

A mixture of linseed oil and vinegar in equal parts makes a useful furniture polish.

Vinegar brightens glass, brass and copper articles.

A small amount of vinegar rubbed over raw meat makes it tender.

Hot vinegar takes away paint stains.

Water and vinegar mixed in equal parts cleans gilt frames.

Diluted vinegar, applied to furniture before polishing, ensures a brilliant polish.

To make a new gas mantle last much longer, soak it for 5 minutes in vinegar, dry and burn off.

To Clean Drains
In hot weather flush all sinks and pipes with very hot, strong soda water at least twice a week.

After washing up, dissolve two tablespoons of soda in boiling water and pour over the sink and down the waste pipe. An efficient disinfectant should also be used occasionally.

To Whiten a Glazed Sink
Wash the sink with hot soapy water to remove all grease, then rinse and put about two or three tablespoonfuls of solution of salts of lemon into the sink, working it in with an old nail brush. When the discoloration has disappeared, remove all trace of the acid by thorough rinsing. (Salts of lemon, being a poison, should only be given to a responsible person to use).

To Clean Tiles
Wash the tiles first with soap and water, being careful not to make the cloth too wet. Then dry them thoroughly, apply a little furniture polish or cream, and rub with a dry duster until bright and shining.

To Clean a Burnt Pan
Fill the pan with hot water then put in 1 tablespoon of salt. Stir till the salt dissolves then leave overnight to let it work. The next day boil the water in the pan and the particles will come off.

To Rid the Kitchen of Smells
Remove the smell of cooking cabbage or cauliflower by adding a little lemon juice to the cooking water.

When stew has been over-salted add a peeled raw potato to the pan and cook for 10 minutes, then take out the potato, which will have absorbed the salt.

To prevent a stew from burning put in a clean marble in the pan. The marble will continuously stir the simmering stew. Do not forget to remove the marble before serving the stew.

To Separate Drinking Glasses
Put the lower glass in very warm water and then pour cold water into the upper.

To Clean Glass
This method is for glass of any kind; mirrors, windows, drinking glasses etc: Wipe the glass with a soft cloth, dampened with ammonia diluted with water. Then wipe dry with a clean dry cloth.

Mix a little dry starch with cold water to the consistency of cream and wash your windows with this, leaving them to dry. To finish, rub the glass with a damp newspaper. This will give your windows a very high polish, without leaving lint or streaks on them.

It is also best to wash your windows on a cloudy day if you want to avoid leaving marks on the glass.

Make your Own Furniture Polish

In the top of a double boiler, or discarded pan put 1 cup of turpentine with 1/2 cup of shredded beeswax. Cook over boiling water stirring all the time, until the wax melts.

When the mixture is completely cool, apply it sparingly to furniture with a soft cloth, then rub with a clean, soft cloth. Any polish that is left may be stored in a jar with a tightly fitting lid.

To Remove Stains

Chocolate and Coffee
Wet the area and rub in borax. Leave it for a few minutes, and then scrub with a clean toothbrush.

Grass
To remove grass stains use cream of tartar, dissolved in a little boiling water. Apply the hot mixture to the stain.

Lipstick on Fabric
Scrape off the lipstick with a dull knife and then rub in petroleum jelly. Wash as usual.

Fruit
To remove fruit stains on any linen, immediately put on powdered starch and let it absorb the stain. Then just brush off the powder and wash as usual.

Wine
To remove a wine stain, rub the area with lemon juice and salt. Then rinse and wash as usual.

Ink
Ink stain on fabric should be treated as quickly as possible, before it has a chance to set.

To remove ink on linen: Wet the spot with milk and then apply dry salt until the stains come out. Or wash the stain with sour milk and soak the fabric overnight.

While the stain is fresh, pour salt, dry starch or another absorbent substance over the stains and then brush it away as it absorbs the ink. Keep the spot wet and continue applying the absorbent until the ink has gone.

To get rid of ink stains from a carpet wash it immediately with milk, rubbing it briskly into the stain with a flannel cloth.

Alternatively, use cream of tartar mixed with a few drops of lemon juice. Make into a paste then spread it on the stain. After one minute, brush off the paste and soak up the residue of the mixture with a sponge, dipped in warm water.

Vegetable
To get rid of vegetable stain from your hands, rub them with a slice of lemon or a raw potato.

Grease
To remove grease stains on a carpet, rub baking soda into the area. Let it stand for about 1 hour then brush the soda out.

To Clean Pure Silk
Grate two clean raw potatoes into each pint of water used. Then strain the water through some cheesecloth. Let the liquor stand until the potato starch it contains settles. Then pour off the clear liquid and bottle it. Lay a clean cloth over a flat hard worktop and place the silk over it. Apply the potato juice with a sponge until the silk is clean. Then rinse the fabric in clean, cold water.

Uses for Tea Leaves
Collect a week's tea leaves in a pail, then pour over them 1 quart of boiling water and leave for 1 hour. Strain and bottle the liquid. This is a splendid gloss maker if used with a soft piece of flannel on mirrors, glasses, or windows. It is also a good cleaner for varnished wood, doors and furniture.

The liquid can also be used for linoleum. A small amount on a soft cloth cleans linoleum better than water. When dry, polish with a soft duster; it gives a shine like beeswax without the dangerous slippery surface.

When pans have been used for fish, the smell can quickly be removed by putting tea leaves in the pan, filling it with cold water and bringing to the boil whilst stirring. Allow to simmer for 5 to 10 minutes. Empty the pan and wipe it dry.

Care of Carpets and Rugs
Carpets and rugs should be cleaned by hand every now and again to freshen up the pile and colours. This can be achieved by wiping them thoroughly with cold water in which tea leaves have been steeped. Remove the tea

leaves from the water, drain, and sprinkle them over the carpet, a strip at a time. With a stiff carpet brush, sweep gently and methodically, going over each strip of carpet until not a particle of dust rises. Sweep up the tea leaves. Finally, wipe the surface of the carpet all over with lukewarm water, to which a little borax has been added, along with some vinegar.

Delicate carpets can be cleaned quickly by brushing in plenty of hot bran. A stiff, perfectly clean brush should be used, if there are any bad stains, reliable carpet soap will remove them. Rinsing must be thoroughly done, with clean cloths, wrung out in fairly hot water.

Coloured wool rugs, which have faded, can be restored by rubbing them with a flannel dipped in warm water to which a little salt and vinegar has been added. Hang the rugs out to dry, on a windy day if possible.

Care of Kid Gloves

Kid gloves last longer and keep their shape better if, as soon as they are taken off, the fingers and thumbs are inflated by being blown into. The gloves should then be laid perfectly flat in a glove box until next wanted.

The grubby finger tips of light-coloured kid gloves can be cleaned by rubbing them with a piece of soft, white India rubber. Clean the rubber on blotting paper as it becomes soiled. Special rubbers can be bought for the purpose.

Very soiled light-coloured gloves will look like new if washed in petrol. Fill a basin with clean petrol and submerse the gloves in it for a few minutes. Wash the cleanest gloves first. Take a small piece of white flannel and rub the glove fingers and dirty parts carefully. Then rub the gloves lightly with the hands with an ordinary washing movement, and wring them out carefully. The cleaned gloves should then be pulled gently into shape, but not stretched, and hung out to dry in the air. Petrol is highly in flammable, and should be kept well away from any naked light.

To clean dark-coloured skin gloves, mix together equal quantities of fuller's earth and powdered alum and rub the gloves all over with the mixture. Leave for two hours, then brush thoroughly to remove the powder.

The secret of keeping gloves in good condition is to clean them before they get too soiled. If gloves are allowed to become very stained it is difficult to regain their new looking appearance.

Care of Stockings

Laundering
Dissolve some shredded soap in a very little hot water. Cool the lather with cold water until it is just warm, and then immerse the stockings. Do not rub but squeeze them until all the dirt is removed. Rinse in two or three tepid waters, squeeze out as much moisture as possible without wringing and dry in the shade.

To take away the too shiny look from new silk stocking, rinse them before wearing them.

To make stockings wear well and keep their colour; soak them before wearing for ten minutes in boiling water to which has been added enough washing blue to colour it.

To Darn Stockings
Darn diagonally across the weave instead of with it; the darn will give as the stocking stretches, thus lessening the tendency of the fabric to break into new holes near to the darn.

Big holes in stockings should have a patch of fine net of the same colour tacked on over the hole; this will form a firm foundation through which to darn.

If the heels of stockings tend to wear out quickly, darn them before wearing, with two strands of fine Mercerised thread. The darn will outlast the stocking. Darning should be done on the right side and over a darning egg.

To Darn Linen
Darn thin places in damask and linen with the finest thread possible. If the fabric is thick, darn on the wrong side, picking up the stitches on the upper threads so that they are invisible on the right side.

If the place is much worn there can be no attempt at concealment and the darn must be done boldly on the right side.

When there is a pattern on the material darn to the shape of it, taking the threads straight up and down. Darning one way may be sufficient but if not, the threads must be crossed.

Caring for Shirts

The cuffs are usually the first parts of a shirt to show signs of wear and tear. The reason for this is easily explained; the fabric in contact with the skin, takes up perspiration, which stubbornly holds the dirt. This means that in washing, extra effort is needed to get them clean and so their life is shortened.

The best way of extending the life of the cuffs is to lightly starch them because this prevents them from getting so dirty. The same applies to collars, which first begin to fray at the fold, where they are in contact with the neck.

Cuffs and collars that are frayed can be turned by unpicking the seams that attach them to the shirt, reversing the pieces, and sewing them back into place. After they have been pressed they will look as good as new

When your shirt fronts wears into a hole where the collar points rub, there is a simple way in which they can be mended. Carefully cut away the lining of the back yoke and unpick the centre seam, and you will have two spare pieces of material that fit exactly on to the fronts. Stitch these in place, covering the holes, and reline the yoke with an odd piece of linen.

Preventing Holes in Socks

To give your socks longer life reverse the order in which they are put on so that each is worn on the right and left foot alternately. It is quite easy to get into a way of knowing how you wore the socks on the previous day. Hang them over a chair when you take them off at night, arranging them as you will wear them on the following day. After you have done this on one or two nights it just becomes a habit. The easier way is to put on clean ones the next day.

Buying and Caring for Shoes

New shoes should fit quite closely to the foot, but should not pinch. Make sure that the sole of the foot and the toes feel quite comfortable.

For use in the country, select shoes with thick soles, there should be room for you to wear a sock in the shoe, for this makes walking more comfortable.

Don't go for a long walk in new shoes, they should be broken in by only wearing them for short periods.

A good way of making new shoes or boots waterproof is to rub the soles with tallow. Continue to rub it in until the leather will absorb no more, the grease will clog the leather and make it waterproof.

It is advisable to have two or three pairs of shoes in commission. Shoes will last much longer if they are given at least 24 hours rest after being worn for a day. Keep them on trees when they are not in use. This not only helps them to keep their shape, but also prevents the leather from cracking.

When cleaning shoes, don't use a knife for scraping off mud and dirt, this weakens the leather. It is better to use a hard brush.

With frequent cleaning, a layer of polish can build up on shoes making the leather look uneven or patchy; wash the polish off with warm water, dry thoroughly and then re-polish.

Wet shoes should be put onto trees as soon as they are taken off and be allowed to dry thoroughly before they are used again. Don't dry shoes in front of the fire, let them dry out slowly and the leather will not be damaged.

One way of drying wet shoes is to fill them with sand; this dries them quickly and preserves their shape. If your new shoes are a bit tight put wet newspaper in them and leave to dry out.

A pebble beach is the greatest enemy for shoes: walking on pebbles cuts the leather. The best way to counter the damage is to rub the cut thoroughly with warm milk, to which a teaspoonful of soda has been added. Wait until the shoes are dry, and then polish in the usual way.

Send shoes to be repaired as soon as wear is apparent. It is false economy to delay repairs. If shoes are repaired promptly, it adds considerably to their life.

To Wash Embroidered Cotton or Linen

Dissolve white soap in hot water, add two teaspoons of borax. If the item is very soiled, boil the articles in the mixture, before or after washing, or both. Squeeze the articles with the hands or draw them through the fingers in the suds until they are clean. Then rinse in clear water, adding to this about half a teaspoon of sugar to one pint of water. Iron without starching.

To Wash White Lace

White lace may be washed by shaking it in a covered jar of very soapy, warm water for 4 to 5 minutes. Repeat with a fresh soap and water solution until the lace is clean. Finally, rinse first with warm water then with cold.

An alternative method is to stretch the lace on a piece of cloth, pinning down all the points. Work over the lace with crumbs from a soft loaf of bread and a soft cloth, using fresh crumbs and a clean cloth, as they become soiled. Shake out the crumbs when the lace is clean.

To Soften Leather Belts

Leather belts and straps tend to harden with age. The best method of making them soft and pliable again is to soak in hot, soapy water for an hour or more. Then hang them up to dry in a cool place, allowing the water to drip out. When the straps or belts are quite dry, polish them well and they will be as good as new.

To Launder an Eiderdown

Eiderdowns, even though large and bulky, can be washed quite successfully at home.

Fill a bath with warm soapsuds and immerse the eiderdown, squeezing it until the water is dirty. Make fresh suds and repeat the process; if the eiderdown is very dirty a third wash may be necessary. To rinse, squeeze the quilt repeatedly in clean warm water, until every particle of soap is removed. Squeeze out as much water as possible then hang the eiderdown out to dry.

To Make Soap from Waste Fat

Weigh out 1lb of fat and place in an old basin or pan, preferably not aluminium. Melt the fat by standing the pan over hot water, while dissolving 2 1/2 oz of caustic soda in 1/2 pint of warm water. Add this solution to the warm fat and stir well. Continue to heat, stirring at intervals and adding more water if necessary. When the mixture becomes milky in appearance and produces a considerable amount of lather on stirring, pour a little of it into a small cup or vessel.

Gradually add a little hot water to this sample. When saponification, (the required chemical change), is complete, a clear, soapy solution should be obtained. Heating must be continued until a test sample gives a clear soapy solution on contact with water. If necessary add a little more water to the mixture to make up for that lost by evaporation. This soap is suitable only for rough cleaning.

An Old Fashioned Cordial for Coughs and Weak Chests

Take 4 new laid eggs, carefully wash their shells, so that all the dirt is removed.

Put them into a large basin without breaking, and pour over the strained juice of 3 large lemons. There should be sufficient juice to cover the eggs.

Leave for 2 days, when the shells will have disappeared. Beat the eggs and juice together thoroughly and add 3/4 pint of best rum, a small jar of honey and about a tablespoonful of glycerine. Mix all these ingredients well and pour into a bottle. Keep tightly corked.

The dose is 1/2 wineglassful when the cough is troublesome, or before going out in the early morning or night air.

Weather Report for 1947

Emilie's diary makes frequent references to the weather. The following report, with its facts and figures, bears out her notes.

Winter
The winter of 1947 was one of the worst on record, and certainly one of the snowiest of the last 150 years. The extreme weather did not set in until late January; mild weather returning to the British Isles in the middle of March.

The end of January saw some very cold nights recorded in parts of southern England. On the night of the 28th/29th Writtle in Essex dropped to -20.6C and on the night of the 29th/30th Elmstone in Kent dipped down to -21.3C. Nationally, these are some of the coldest nights ever measured in late January.

February 1947 was very dull, windy and frosty. For example, at Kew Gardens in London the sun shone for just 17 hours the whole month, compared to an average of 61 hours. Between the 2nd and 22nd the sun didn't shine at all. The dull weather did have one advantage though; it prevented really cold nights from occurring until the end of the month when parts of Southern England, Woburn, Luton and Stratford-upon-Avon dropped to between -17C and -21C.

In spite of the absence of really cold nights for much of the month, February 1947 was nevertheless very cold; on the Central England temperature series it was, measuring -19C on the series, the coldest February since records began in 1659. Average maximum temperatures for the month were close to freezing in many places and in Oxford temperatures were below freezing from 6pm on the 10th to 6am on the 26th. Further east, ice floes were observed in the sea off Whitstable in Kent. In Dorset, every night, between 16th January and 11th March, except 2nd and 3rd February, was frosty.

Spring
March was even worse than February. The first half of the month remained wintry. Blizzards and heavy snow affected the country from time to time. For example, on the 4th to 6th, a snowstorm affecting most of England and

Wales deposited 40cm snow in Birmingham and caused drifts close to 5m high in parts of Southern Wales. Southern England was affected by an ice storm. Temperatures dropped sharply during this period and one of the coldest March nights on record followed, when on the 4th lows dipped to -21C in Braemar, Peebles and Houghall, in the northern half of Britain. Later in the month, on the 16th, gales affected the UK and in some parts of southern England gusts were close to 100 mph.

The second half of March was generally milder and very wet, with frequent downpours. The onset of mild weather also led to a rapid thaw of the winter's snow. This in turn caused some serious flooding. Some places experienced their worst flooding in 250 years. In Stratford-on-Avon the floods of 1947 would be the worst until the late 1990's.

Floods in York on the 24th March were the worst since 1831, whilst severe floods in the fenland area of East Anglia led to the setting up of a flood protection scheme. There was even a brief return to winter on the 27th, when snow fell in some places, including Brighton.

Taking England and Wales as a whole, March 1947 is the wettest March on record with 177.5mm recorded on the England and Wales precipitation series. Many parts of the UK recorded more than 3 times their average March rainfall in 1947. Torquay recorded nearly 3.75, their average March rainfall. Most of England and Wales recorded more than 23 days with rain in March, and Birmingham recorded the greatest number of rain days; 28 in all. The Central London weather station at Camden Square recorded 122 hours of rain. Between 1888, when records here began, and 1947 only two other months recorded more hours of rain; March 1916 (134) and December 1927 (127).

Spring 1947 was the 4th wettest on record on the England and Wales precipitation series; only those of 1782, 1818 and 1979 were wetter. In the case of spring 1947 this was due to the exceptional wetness in March. Rainfall in April and May was close to average.

Summer
The summer of 1947 is the 6th warmest on record, dating back to 1659. Only the summers of 1976, 1826, 1995, 1846 and 1983 have been hotter. (For the sake of convenience in record keeping meteorologists take summer as starting on 1st June and ending on 31st August). The summer of 1947

started momentously. Between 30th May and 3rd June temperatures reached 31.7C or more somewhere in south-eastern England every day during this period. Since 1850 this is the hottest this part of the year has ever been. The heat wave peaked on June 3rd when temperatures in London and Waddington reached 34.4C in London. This proved to be to be the hottest day of the whole year.

Between July 14th and 19th there were widespread and severe thunderstorms. Some of the worst downpours occurred on the 16th in parts of Surrey. Between 110 and 130mm rain fell in just a matter of hours in the Wisely-Byfleet area; in Wisley just over 100mm rain fell in 75 minutes. Rainfall records in Surrey date back to 1865 and at the time this was a record for the greatest 24 hours rainfall total in Surrey. This record may still stand today. This was an extremely localised downpour, as just 18 miles away no rain at all was recorded on that date. Further north, Shrewsbury recorded 99.3mm rain in downpours on the 19th July.

August was a hot, dry month. On the Central England temperature series it is the 4th hottest August on record with a value of 18.6C; only those of 1995, 1997 and 1975 have been hotter since records began in 1659. Average maximum temperatures in many places were between 23 and 27C, and even on the generally cooler North Sea coasts they were up to around 20C. The 16th and 17th were two particularly hot days; Southampton, for example, recorded 33.9C both days and Bournemouth also reached 33.9C on the 16th. On the Isle of Wight and the Scilly Isles the 16th proved to be a record breaking day. The 32.8C measured at both Newport and Ryde on the Isle of Wight and the 27.8C recorded at St. Mary's on the Scilly Isles are the highest temperatures ever recorded on these islands.

Most of August, as well as early September, were very dry. Taking England and Wales as a whole it was the second driest August since records began in 1766. Only August 1995 (9.1mm) is drier, whilst August 1912 (192.9) is the wettest. Some places, Peterborough, Greenock and Aberdeen recorded almost no rain whilst central London and Oxford were dry from the 5th onwards through the rest of the month. Wellingborough, in Northamptonshire was drier still, recording no rain between July 29th and September 10th, a period of 44 days. In central London there was just 2 hours rain, measured at the Camden Square Weather Station; at the time the second least in August since records began there in 1881; in August 1940 it rained for just 20 minutes in the whole month.

Autumn

September started off warm and dry. As late as the 15th and 16th temperatures reached 28.9C in Southend and measured 31C in Norwich on the 15th and 16th. September 1947 went on to be the 20th warmest in records dating back to 1659.

October was, taking England and Wales as a whole, the 6th driest October since records began in 1766, and the 3rd driest October in the whole of the 20th century. The England and Wales precipitation series measured 22.2mm compared to 8.8mm in the driest October on record, 1781, and 218.1mm in the wettest, 1903. In central London, Camden Square measured just 3 hours worth of rain, the lowest since records began in 1881.

November 1947 saw frequent periods of heavy rain in northern and western Britain. The 11th was a particularly wet day with more than 75mm rain falling in several parts of Yorkshire and Lancashire. Widespread, disruptive snow does not usually occur in England in November, but it did in 1947, many places seeing some snow in the middle of the month.

The long periods of dry weather in September and October allowed autumn 1947 to become the 6th driest on record in England and Wales. Since records began in 1766, only the autumns of 1978, 1817, 1805, 1788 and 1784 have been drier. It was also close to being one of the 20 warmest autumns since temperature records began in 1659.

EXTRACT FROM LETTERS FROM LAVENDER COTTAGE

Dear Angelique,

I expect that you, like me, have a morning routine; since my computer became an important part of my retirement mine is to put on the kettle for tea and get connected to the Internet and look at my email and web site messages.

On April 15th 2001 this message appeared on the www.hastings.uk.net notice board:-

"Does anyone know if the house, Lavender Cottage, The Ridge, Hastings, is still there? A cousin of mine lived there for years. I believe she died in 1955. We have many letters written to my aunt, who sent her parcels during WW II and after, when supplies were short. They are an interesting account of that period of history"
Wendy Johnson from Canada

I emailed Wendy, confirming that the house still exists; the location is quite close to my village. I later emailed her a photo of the cottage, asking if it would be possible to see the letters. Wendy copied all of the nearly 100 letters and sent them to me.

As I read them I became drawn into the daily doings of their writer, Miss Emilie Crane and her house companions and wanted to share the pleasure of the letters with others. I began an email correspondence with Wendy in Canada, which, incidentally, has become as interesting as the letters from the 1940s and 1950s.

Angelique, would you be a sounding board and adviser to a compilation of Emilie's letters? I think that you will become as fond of Emily as I have. Although she was a stranger to me, when I started to read the letters I felt as if I had actually met her.

During my childhood in the nineteen-thirties and forties I met many ladies like Miss Crane; my parents, who were a cook and gardener, frequently had employers like her. Before I was old enough for school and during the holidays, there was often no one to look after me when my mother worked, so I had to go her employer's house and make myself scarce, somewhere in the kitchen, garden or outbuildings. There, sometimes I met the mistresses of the houses and I was rather in awe of them.

Usually, these ladies, raised in comfortable circumstances, were kindly and well educated and did, 'good works' for their church, charitable societies and local, impoverished families. They did not waste much effort on being fashionable. They wore a comfortable ensemble of sensible shoes and stockings, felt hats and tweedy, woolly garments. They had simple, 'bun', hair styles and good, English complexions. They had a jaunty humour and a lively sense of duty. I think Emilie Crane was a perfect example of this breed.

Emilie's letters of thanks, for food parcels, sent from Canada by her cousin Marion and her friend Beatrice, are a cheerful and vivid account of coping with the restrictions of war and post war austerity and the trials of the advancing years of herself and her two house companions; her life-long friend Miss Clare Marriott and their mutual friend, Miss Edith Lake. I hope you enjoy your meeting with Emilie and find her life and character as heart-warming, funny and inspiring as I have.

Love from,

Victoria.

Lavender Cottage,
The Ridge,
Hastings,
East Sussex

June 9th 1942.

My Dear Marion,

I can't tell you how delighted I was to receive your lovely parcel this morning; it was a welcome surprise and more than kind of you to send it. I don't know how you came to choose the things most needed and such acceptable items. I think the things we have most missed here are butter and fruit; all the fats are so scarce and the rations do not allow us much, so we shall revel in nice bread and butter. As for oranges, the small consignment sent over is reserved for children under six, which is as it should be, therefore, we shall rejoice in the fruit juice.

The tea will be a treat; I gave my ration coupons to Miss Marriott, who can only drink china tea. A friend had some Orange Pekoe tea sent from British Columbia and I have been enjoying that, so now it is my turn to smile! I am very intrigued with the egg powder and shall try it at the first opportunity. I have scoured Hastings for a saucepan cleaner, how did you think of that? Soap and sugar are of course rationed strictly. I can get saccharine but I do not care much for it; such sickly stuff. The serviettes will be very useful as the paper shortage is acute. Hence the notepaper I am using, taken from some old volumes, from a period when they used better paper than they do now. My best thanks for everything and the kind thoughts that came with them.

I do hope the above remarks do not sound as if we are in a bad way; it is only that things are in short supply. Lord Woolten has done very well; we all think that food distribution is better than in the Great War. We do miss some things, naturally, but we expect that in a terrible war. I think the light is beginning to come through at last, don't you? Hitler is not having a very pleasant time. All day the fighters and bombers go over us on their way to France and Germany. They are Canadians, Americans, British, Polish, etc; we know they do some damage. We have had two raids recently, they were not nice and there were a good many casualties. My other friend's sister is an ambulance driver and she tells us some sad stories but everyone here is wonderfully cheerful and none doubt of ultimate victory. We had an exciting time last week when the wounded from the Commando raid on France were brought to the hospital here; I am sorry to say that one died.

I wish I could do more to help but one's age is against it. (Emilie is 71 years old at this time) I took the first aid course and went to help in a First Aid Post but it was so damp I got pleurisy after three months and the doctor would not let me go there again. So I went for an anti-gas course and received a certificate, but fortunately the Germans have not resorted to gas. I offered myself for clerical work but they wanted younger people, so I fell back on door-to-door collecting for the National Savings Campaign and that has been successful. One can do knitting of course, but it isn't exciting to knit all the time; some of my pullovers would fit a large-sized giant! The garden is a great joy and we really have done well with vegetables but fruit is very shy and does not like the Ridge climate.

Well my dears I hope you will forgive this rambling on, there is little news to give you and each day is the repetition of another; planes overhead, air raid alerts and wireless news.

By the way, I have not mentioned my family. They are all well except my sister-in-law who is now in a nursing home. Her mind has gone but she is happy and knows little of the war, which is a mercy, poor thing. I believe my nephew is well and he looks after his mother. Please give my love to everyone and much to yourself, with renewed thanks,

Yours affectionately

Emilie. PS this letter is a scrawl but the paper is not easy to write on

Dear Angelique,

I am not surprised you found some things in Emilie's letters difficult to understand, especially her pre-occupation with food. Like you, I admire Emilie when she reveals her determination to do some wartime duty, in spite of age and not very good health.

With typical understatement she refers to the Hastings daylight raids as 'not being nice', when, in fact, there was considerable loss of life, many casualties and the destruction of scores of buildings in the town. Hastings was in the front line when it came to air raids and in 1942 the town was repeatedly the victim of low-level, tip and run raids, which happened without warning and left residents in a constant state of fear.

Emilie probably did not know any details of the commando raid, which brought the wounded soldiers to Hastings, perhaps it was a reconnoitre raid, before the major commando attack that happened at Dieppe in August 1942. There were many Canadians stationed in Hastings and its surroundings during that period; there is nothing in the local paper about a commando raid but you would not expect that in wartime.

A Hastings man, Ivor White, aged 76, who was teenaged member of the Home Guards in 1942, told me about a Maidstone & District Bus garage, which used to stand at the bottom of Lower Lake in Battle, where he helped the 8th Canadian Reconnoitre Battalion to prepare army vehicles, mainly Jeeps, for a 'secret' raid on the French coast. The Jeep's exhaust pipes had to be lengthened and made vertical, and the distributors sealed, to enable the vehicles to drive into the sea from the landing craft, which often meant submersion to a depth of three or four feet in the sea-water. He said: 'I believe that the destination was Dieppe; many Canadians did not return'.

Noel Care, now aged 78, did duty on the Home Front, as Civil Defence Worker, in Hastings during WWII; he told me that the first large contingent of overseas soldiers in the town were Canadians, who were stationed in empty hotels and other abandoned properties. 'These friendly young men were very popular with locals', he said. They all disappeared in early August, prior to the Dieppe commando raids.

The Lord Woolten, to whom Emilie refers, was the Minister of Food and he is particularly remembered today by older people for his wartime, economy recipe for Woolton pie, which was a dish of pastry and vegetables. Today's vegetarians would probably love it but it did not go down too well in the Britain of the 1940s, with its predominately meat-eating population. About this time, my mother invented some little potato cakes, which were flavoured with lots of onion and a scrap of our cheese ration. She put them on the table saying, 'Try it!' and this tasty, experimental dish was named 'triots' thereafter.

I wonder if Emilie's remark, 'I scoured Hastings for a saucepan cleaner' was an intentional pun; it was the kind of quip I think she would have enjoyed, don't you? She refers to the writing paper shortage; this, of course, extended to lack of paper for personal hygiene. With that lack, and the constant drive to salvage (recycle) everything, I can tell you very little paper was put in the dustbin in wartime!

It was not only the household at Lavender Cottage that was pre-occupied with food; frequent announcements and opinions on the matter appeared in the local paper, The Hastings and St Leonards Observer.

In the week of 13th June 1942 residents were informed that the new issue of ration books would take about two to three weeks to distribute. The Ministry of Food said it strongly disapproved of shopkeepers who tried to get new registrations from customers by unfair methods or conveyed the suggestion that one retailer can offer greater security than another, in the supply of rationed foods..

In the same period we were reminded that war is not all action when we read that three WAAF Hastings girls, Aircraft Women Haste, Hills and Munday, were appealing for a gramophone, adding, "It is a good life we are leading but it gets a bit monotonous." In June 1942, Double British Summer Time was in effect, evenings were very long, with blackout time not starting till after 11.00pm.

James, the Lavender Cottage cat, who we meet later, might or might not have been pleased to know that C H Gaunt of Hastings, the Consultant Superintendent of The Peoples' Dispensary for Sick Animals, published instructions on how to make a gas-proof cat and dog box, which the pet should be encouraged to sleep in permanently, in preparation for the worst.

In the previous month the British Government postponed its plans for fuel rationing after widespread opposition but there must have been some chilly lower limbs as the patriotic 'bare legs for fashion', began to take on. I cannot see Emilie and her friends subscribing to this daring contribution to victory!

Love from

Victoria.

Letters from Lavender Cottage

by Victoria Seymour

Hastings in WWII and Austerity

A collection of recently discovered letters, posted from Hastings to Canada between 1942 and 1955, inspired Victoria Seymour to compile a part-biography of their writer, Emilie Crane.

In her retirement, Emilie shared a house in Hastings, England, with her two friends, Clare and Edith and their much-loved cat, James. The almost one hundred letters Emilie sent to her Canadian cousins were initially of thanks for the food parcels they had supplied to the Lavender Cottage household in WWII and throughout the following years of harsh austerity. The letters also detail the lively and kind-hearted Emilie Crane's domestic and personal life and follow the joint fortunes of the three ageing women.

Victoria Seymour has rounded the story by adding contemporary national, local and autobiographical material. "Letters From Lavender Cottage" is a touching, human story with an informative narrative.

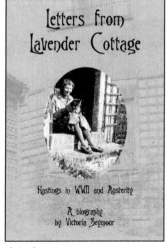

Letters from Lavender Cottage

Hastings in WWII and Austerity

A biography by Victoria Seymour

ISBN: 0-9543901-0-5   www.victoriaseymour.com

Court in the Act

written & compiled by Victoria Seymour

Crime and Policing in WWII Hastings
Foreword by Ann Widdecombe M.P.

Victoria Seymour's Court in the Act, which completes her trilogy, concentrates on the work of the police force, the magistrates' and other courts in WWII Hastings. As the effects of war took hold, there was hardly any aspect of home front life that was not controlled by some Government Act, Regulation or Order, putting even more pressure on already overworked police officers.

There passed before the courts a parade of 'spies', aliens, pacifists, looters, wartime racketeers and small-time criminals. Added to these were thousands of usually law-abiding people who found themselves in court for flouting often not properly understood laws. Sentences were handed down that sounded like something out of 19th Century history: A fine for stealing one onion from an allotment, a few apples from a tree or vegetable peelings from a dustbin or a month in prison for allowing light to escape from behind a curtain.

Meanwhile, the formidable Government Enforcers stalked the land incognito, seeking to trap unwary traders and citizens and bring them to justice. Police Court reports from the period 1939 to 1945 give an insight into a little discussed aspect of WWII. 'Vigilant', The Hastings and St Leonards Observer 1940s columnist, provides a background, with comment on the foibles and morals of a seaside town under fire.

Fact met fiction, when in 2004 Victoria Seymour was asked by Greenlit Productions, who film Foyle's War, the WWII detective television drama set in Hastings, to assist in re-creating a Hastings' wartime magistrates' court for series three.

ISBN: 0-9543901-2-1   www.victoriaseymour.com

Letters to Hannah

written & compiled by Victoria Seymour

WWII Recollections
of Hastings & South East England

Letters to Hannah looks at WWII on the Home Front through the eyes of those who lived in Hastings and South East England from September 1939 to December 1945. It also enlarges on the historical background covered in its companion book, Letters from Lavender Cottage.

Letters to Hannah visits the lives of ordinary people, who endured extraordinary times. Among many others is the account of a Battle lad, born in a cottage beside the famous 1066 battlefield. Aged fifteen he enlisted as a Home Guard, the youngest member in the country at that time, a Hastings, wartime milk delivery girl details her working and family life under fire and a young first aid volunteer highlights the horrors of bomb and machine gun attacks on civilians. 'Letters to Hannah' is rich in anecdotes and information on food rationing and shortages, the blackout, air raids, population evacuation and civil defence. The book provides a moving and factual account of wartime Hastings, the town which features in the ITV, WWII detective fiction series, Foyle's War.

Victoria Seymour links this, her second WWII social history, with a series of autobiographical letters to the future, describing her war-troubled childhood to her newborn, 21st century granddaughter, Hannah. Extracts from Letters to Hannah were included in the BBC Radio 4 history series, The Archive Hour, in July 2003.

ISBN: 0-9543901-1-3   www.victoriaseymour.com

HOST FAMILIES WANTED

Written & compiled
by Victoria Seymour

For over half century Hastings has been host to hundreds of thousands of young people from all over the world.

Host Families Wanted, the true story of overseas English language students in Hastings, is approached with the enthusiasm for detail that Victoria Seymour's regular readers expect of her.

She recounts her own experiences as student host mother, the company director of a family-run, Hastings based language school and how the work affected her life and family.

The problem of street offences against students is considered, as are the efforts of the police and the local authority to reduce the crime and protect students.

To enrich the story there are interviews with local host families and the students' teachers. In a set of essays, a group of today's overseas students comment frankly on Hastings and their hosts.

If you are a host family, have been, or are thinking of becoming one, this book is for you.

ISBN: 0-9543901-5-6
www.victoriaseymour.com

The Long Road to Lavender Cottage

written & compiled by Victoria Seymour

The now famous occupant of Lavender Cottage, Emilie Crane, returns, to let us back into her life and the daily doings of her neighbours on the Ridge. What was the truth about the supposed nudist colony opposite Lavender Cottage? Was the guest house close by really a haven for left wing agitators and a bolt hole for a scandalous occultist, Aleister Crowley?

Victoria Seymour has meticulously researched the background and history of a period and place that was peopled not just by locals leading ordinary lives but by notable figures from the worlds of literature, religion, the arts, healing, politics and entertainment, including Joanna Lumley.

We are given glimpses into the Ridge's former large Victorian houses, cottages, farms, institutions and businesses and the lives of their occupants in peace time and war. The Long Road to Lavender Cottage also reveals dramatic events in Emilie Crane's daily life that she was not able to write about in her wartime letters, for fear of the government censor.

ISBN: 0-9543901-4-8   www.victoriaseymour.com

The Slow Turning Tide

Written & compiled
by Victoria Seymour

Victoria Seymour's The Slow Turning Tide looks back to over a half a century ago, when Hastings and St Leonards faced the long task of recovering from WWII. With her talent for uncovering intriguing detail Victoria features stories of Hastings citizens, rebuilding their lives, homes and careers, marrying and raising families, while enduring austerity and nine post-war years of rationing and shortage of everything, including houses.

Peacetime Hastings was the scene of two conflicts - the developers against the preservationists and the down-to-earth holiday traders opposing the die-hards, who yearned to see the town established as a select residential and coastal resort, a pre-war ideal that never really existed. In spite of controversy, Hastings soon reasserted itself as a popular holiday spot with a round of carnivals, processions, stage shows, galas, beauty contests and all the fun of the seaside.

Throughout the book the commentator on post-war news is Frederick Goodsell, the editor of the Hastings and St Leonards Observer and also its weekly columnist under the pen name "Vigilant". Goodsell, seeming part Churchill, part Mr Pooter, rails against the evils of progress and what he sees as the declining moral values of his town.

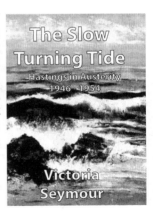

ISBN 0-9543901-6-7
www.victoriaseymour.com